Occupational Analysis
Techniques & Procedures

Occupational Analysis

Techniques & Procedures

Revision of *Analysis Technique for Instructors* and *Trade and Job Analysis*

VERNE C. FRYKLUND, Ph.D.

Emeritus President, Stout State University, Menomonie, Wisconsin

THE BRUCE PUBLISHING COMPANY, New York

Cover and chapter opening photographs supplied by the National Aeronautics and Space Administration, Public Information Office, Cocoa Beach, Florida.

TO ADAH

Library of Congress Catalog Card Number: 78-116786

The Bruce Publishing Company, New York
Collier-Macmillan Canada, Ltd., Toronto, Ontario

Made in the United States of America

Preface

This book was prepared for teachers in service and for persons who are in training to become teachers. It is a streamlined modification of earlier plans of analysis. The author himself not only has assisted technicians and other workers in analyzing their assignments; he has been a worker himself and has served as an educator/teacher and training officer for many years. He has been interested in studying and experimenting with analysis to make it as understandable and as practical as possible.

The plan of analysis presented in this book can be applied to any occupation which is sufficiently involved to require instruction for anyone who wishes to learn it. The underlying principle of analysis is simple and easy to understand. In every kind of work in the world which is creative, that is, where things are produced, or when ideas are developed, where and when there is human achievement, two things are likely to be present. There are *elements* on one hand and something comparable to *problems* on the other. And there is a similarity of subject-matter organization to that of mathematics. Just as in arithmetic, the elements must be identified and taught. These elements must be distinguished from the problems, but yet they must be applied in typical problems as they are taught. For example, in a technical occupation, objects that are made can be compared to problems in arithmetic. The fundamental operations and information necessary in combination to produce something can be compared to the elements of arithmetic. An understanding of this important principle, as covered in this book, would be exceedingly helpful in analyzing almost any occupation for instructional purposes.

Even though it is assumed that perfection is possible, those who know better will say that human nature is so variable that it would be impossible to discover a formula of action that would fit perfectly every training situation. However, experience has shown that this plan of analysis has a wide variety of applications and is simpler, more practical, more easily understood than earlier plans. This technique can be applied with but few exceptions in analyzing many occupations that are not classified in the skilled trades but yet are involved enough to require systematic training. The title, OCCUPATIONAL ANALYSIS, TECHNIQUES AND PROCEDURES, is used because of this broad intent.

The first edition was used rather intensively in training in the military during World War II. The instructional units taught in the Armored School at Fort Knox, Kentucky, were determined by this technique. The analysis by the author of combat tank repair at Rock Island Arsenal was likewise determined.

There are changes throughout the book that clarify the study of analysis, but there is no basic change in the technique. A chapter on problem-solving is included because of the growing interest in a proved procedure that will bring system into the problem-solving approach in industrial teaching.

The author acknowledges the helpful criticisms of the many instructors who have used this book. Particular recognition is given the staff of instructor trainers who worked under the author's direction at Fort Knox and who gave this book critical and intensive use. They proved that the analysis technique has wide application in other than strictly mechanical pursuits.

Some parts of this book have appeared in some form in magazine articles in *Industrial Arts and Vocational Education* and in the *Industrial Education Magazine*. Certain references to details and authority appear in footnotes, and acknowledgements to the authors and publishers are thus recognized. Many persons have contributed unknowingly to this work, particularly students and in-service teachers who have, by their critical consideration of analysis procedures, pointed to the need for and influenced the present writing.

The second edition was translated into Japanese, Chinese, Spanish, Persian, Hebrew, and Turkish.

The author is grateful for the valuable suggestions offered by Dr. Thomas Fleming, Dr. J. A. Jarvis, Dr. H. H. London, Dr. J. W. Giachino, Dr. V. H. Hardt, Dr. W. J. Micheels, Dr. G. S. Wall, Dr. Dewey Barich, Dr. H. Robert Kinker, and Mr. Lee W. Ralston.

VERNE C. FRYKLUND

Contents

Occupational Analysis

This occupational analysis technique is for initial training and upgrading of training personnel. It is a technique by means of which the essential elements of an occupation, or any part of an occupation or activity, are identified and listed for instructional purposes. It is an inventory procedure, somewhat like the listing of the goods on the shelves and in the warehouse of a store. The proprietor must know the names and exact numbers of items or units of goods that constitute his complete offering to the public. He must systematize the inventory procedure when he takes it so he knows the status of the supply at a given time. The goods on the shelf are labeled, but the elements in an occupation do not become labeled until they have been identified by means of analysis, the educational inventory procedure which requires special training in the technique of identifying the elements.

In order to teach an occupation or a subject or an activity there first must be an inventory of the elements to be taught. Most occupations are not so adequately covered in books as are subjects like mathematics. And perhaps this is a good thing because industry changes. The analysis procedure records the units as they exist at the time when the inventory is taken. Much is said in modern educational procedures about making school achievement as much like world achievement as possible. The present analysis technique does this for all areas in which it is applied. Through this procedure the essential elements of an occupation are brought into the instructional situation whether for training in the formal school or for training on the job.

Just as there must be system and orderly procedure in making a business inventory, so must there be system and orderly procedure in making an analysis for teaching purposes. But the system must be simple and readily usable, otherwise it would have doubtful value. Certain techniques that lead to system as well as to simplicity are necessary, and when they are followed carefully, the analysis results in a practical and thoroughgoing inventory of essential elements of the occupation under consideration. It is not an overnight procedure, however. It takes time— time carefully expended. Once an analysis has been made, it should be reviewed periodically to determine whether there have been technological changes that would modify the listing.

Habits and the Occupational Expert

Analysis should be considered first in the training given to an occupational expert who is to become an instructor. When such a person is to become a teacher, he usually does not know how to identify the things to teach. He usually has considerable difficulty in discovering the elements to be taught, elements which he himself has mastered. The fundamental elements learned by an individual become habitual as experience increases. Because little attention is paid to things habitual, most of us hardly realize that we have habits. Things we learn thoroughly become habits, and so the fundamental elements of an occupation become habits to the individual. He may be an expert with many years of experience, but it is difficult for him to determine what should be taught at the outset in his new job of teaching. Even though he himself may have been taught in a systematic way, what he learned has become habit. Analysis is therefore necessary in order to provide an adequate inventory of the elements that have become life habits.

The analysis technique should be studied by all teachers of so-called practical subjects in order that emphasis in teaching may be properly placed on the elements to be taught as distinguished from the problems to be solved. Teachers of industrial subjects make instruction realistic by observing these lessons.

Analysis is also valuable in clarifying the work of experienced instructors whose training lacks this exceedingly fundamental procedure. An experienced teacher can profit much by taking a course in analysis. It is refreshing. Those who have had analysis find their instructional travel defined, they know where they are going, they know what to teach and the order of teaching the lesson. Even an occasional repetition of the study of analysis is helpful to experienced teachers.

Analysis in Education for Industry

Analysis is exceedingly important as long as education for industry is necessary. The term *job analysis* appeared early in vocational and general educational literature and it has caught the attention of people who are interested in curriculum procedures in all fields of education. It also has become a catchword and is used by persons outside of education in connection with work that has no relation to training. Many who have attempted to use analysis in education, however, have had difficulty because in early stages of its development much detail was required and there remained much to be desired in clearness. The instructor became confused and burdened in his attempts to follow the details while instructing.[1] When a system requires too much of the teacher's attention it should be modified and simplified, or abandoned. System must clarify instructional procedures and not complicate them. Experience through the years has made it possible critically to reconsider analysis and simplify it and extend its practical usefulness. It has come to be one of the most important and lasting contributions in the improvement of curriculum procedures in all areas of education.

1. See Fig. 16, p. 119.

Any occupation that involves fundamental procedures can be analyzed for instructional purposes. Most occupations in which there is human achievement, and where past experience must be drawn upon for further achievement, can be analyzed and listed so they can be taught in an orderly and systematic way.

The fact that there are technological changes in industry does not mean that the time will come when training no longer will be needed. Indeed, it is true that as technical changes take place, changes are also being made in the status of occupations. Many of them are broken up; new occupations appear, but simultaneously the needs and demands for training are increased. Analysis of present-day occupations brings industrial training up to date, whereas education in general, because of its reliance on book content, lags behind in attempting to keep pace with conditions in the world outside of school. Critics of education say that education is slow in making adjustment. Because of the availability of the analysis technique, education is in position to keep pace.

There should be constant seeking of up-to-date teaching content in every area under instruction. It is through the analysis technique that the content materials are provided for the course of study. The inventory of instructional units in a given occupation is usually exhaustive enough to provide up-to-date content material for several courses of study.

The teacher who has analyzed his activity has identified the daily lessons. The first major effort toward planning for a demonstration, preparing visual aids, or for writing instruction sheets should be the identification by analysis of the instructional units involved. Analysis, therefore, should come first in a training program for technical teachers.

Analysis in Underdeveloped Countries

Establishing training in instructional techniques in underdeveloped countries is based on analysis. The know-how involved in processing raw materials into finished goods has its beginnings in identification of the elements that must be mastered in carrying on such training. The first step in preparing teachers and equipping them with effective training materials starts with occupational analysis. The translation of this book into six languages attests to the necessity and value of this technique.

System and Order and Progress

Most people recognize the importance of system and order in modern life. Success and progressive achievement depend upon a logical approach rather than upon chance. The necessity for system and order is manifest in periods of rapid change even more than under static conditions. In fact, system is characteristic of modern progress. Progress, it is true, depends upon change, but considerable permanency and organization are essential for lasting achievement. In any worthwhile creative activity, order, regularity, and sequence are necessary for growth and development. The teacher who can analyze his work is likely to be systematic and orderly in organizing instruction. He has acquired an ability that will lead to greater and greater professional growth and achievement for himself as well as for his students.

Modern Industrial Workers

People in education and other areas of world activity are not always clear in their understanding of workers in industry. Persons who do simple repetitive work are confused with skilled mechanics, both as to the terms used to identify them and the work they do. It is often said that skilled mechanics are diminishing in number because of the machine and automation, and therefore training is not needed to replace persons who are assumed to be displaced or retired. Currently the shortage of skilled workers is so great that the federal government has appropriated several million dollars in special funds for training and retraining. The redirection of skilled workers and the maintenance of space-age equipment loom as national problems. (As technology changes, training and retraining become increasingly important.)

It is desirable for teachers of technical subjects to know the facts concerning the influence of mass production and automation on training needs and the differences in types of workers. They should at least be more familiar with conditions surrounding their work than are persons with superficial knowledge who write to inform the public to the disadvantage of youth. An important step in studying analysis is to study the worker as described in Chapter 2.

Kinds of Analysis

There have been doubtful uses of the term *job analysis* (see Chapter 3). Many kinds of research activities in industry and business are referred to as job analyses. Because they are thus identified, their users have attempted to employ them in identifying training elements, but usually with little success. Brief descriptions of the more common analysis procedures which have been confused with the analysis technique for training purposes are therefore necessary.

Making an Analysis

In order to learn how to analyze successfully for training purposes, it is first necessary to clarify the terminology involved as is done in Chapters 4 and 5. There are a few technical terms that have much to do with clarifying the analysis procedure and with identifying the elements to be taught. It is desirable therefore that such terms be defined at the outset.

Application in Technical Occupations

There are two major classes of technical occupations which require slightly different approaches in analysis. They are custom trades and service trades and they appear in small shops and in large production plants. Custom trades involve the production of things, while service trades involve repair, overhaul, or installation. Because there is a difference in their functions, there is a minor difference in the analysis approach, but the general procedure of analysis is the same in both kinds of occupations. The general principle of analysis applies with but minor modifications in other areas of work that require training.

When the elements have been inventoried, it is necessary to arrange a relative order to be followed in teaching them, otherwise there is a possibility that something of advanced nature may be taught in place of something elementary. One of the reasons for the need of analysis is that it provides a way of systematizing instruction. Any attempts at analysis without knowing its techniques are likely to result in material that is confusing rather than helpful.

Application in Other Areas

It is impossible to provide an exact formula for analyzing all areas of work, but the procedure described in the following chapters is practical. There may be need for some change in terms when areas outside of industrial production are analyzed, but a good rule to follow is that in any area of work where things are created, whether of the head or of the hand, there is likely to be found a content arrangement similar to that of arithmetic. There are elements on one hand and problems, or something similar, on the other. Whether there is a project, an idea, a bill of goods sold, a nursing assignment, or a police assignment, standard elements are likely to be involved and there is something similar to a problem to be solved. The elements must be identified and listed because they are the things to be taught, not the problems. *We do not teach problems; we teach the elements by applying them in solving typical problems.*

Learning and Teaching

After the elements to be taught have been listed, there remains the need to find the most effective ways to teach them. This takes much study and practice. A single book on teaching methods alone would not be adequate. Several books covering various aspects of teaching, and several courses, plus the important factor of experience, are all necessary to make a good teacher. However, there are a few elementary principles that deserve immediate study and which will help the new teacher in getting started while he makes a more thorough study of the techniques of teaching. A few of these elementary principles are presented in Chapter 9 following the instruction on analysis.

Course Development

It should be made clear that the material obtained by analysis is not a course of study. Course of study development follows analysis. The analysis may provide materials for several courses of study. The analysis is the inventory of an educational store; the course of study is an educational bill of goods taken from the more complete store and made ready for delivery by means of good teaching and management. This, too, requires detailed study and cannot be learned in a few hours. But in Chapter 10 of this book are some helpful suggestions for those who must arrange course materials immediately following instruction on analysis. This chapter is helpful also to experienced teachers and is a guide for committees responsible for course development. It is helpful in unifying the efforts of the latter. It is helpful in clarifying the purpose and place of analysis.

Problem-Solving

Youth of today must fit into a more complicated environment than did youth of fifty years ago. There are many new materials, new ways to do things, and new things to do. While change will continue, there is an exceedingly important ability that will remain a constant need, one which education must provide through the ages. This ability is not just confined to a few scientific areas; it is necessary in all human endeavors. It is the ability to solve problems, and it is required of all people who aspire to lead and create. All areas of education must continue to provide opportunities for development of such ability.

Preparation for all useful occupations should include guided experiences that will lead to the development of problem-solving ability. Analysis provides the specific subject matter needed in forming solutions to problems typical of industrial production. The chapter devoted to problem-solving provides a description of a proved approach based on problem-solving in mathematics. Here purposeful thinking is apparent, and provides a pattern for training in purposeful thinking in all human endeavors.

Written Instructions

Success and advancement in technical pursuits, out of school as well as in school, is associated with ability to read technical literature. Written instructions for teaching are therefore recommended not only for the technical information gained, but also for developing the habit of reading technical literature and thus keeping abreast with changing technology. This provides a practical stimulus for the realization of the importance of reading in everyday life. Analysis precedes instruction-sheet writing and preparation of other instructional aids. Since they are related, a chapter covering important information on the writing and the use of instruction sheets is included.

ANALYSIS NECESSARY IN INDUSTRIAL-ARTS EDUCATION

In the upper levels of high school, industrial arts is offered largely for its technical-training values. The major difference between well-organized, well-equipped, and well-taught industrial arts in senior high school and training for a technical occupation is in the time devoted to shopwork. The former covers a less extended period in terms of weeks and usually there are two hours per day in the shop, whereas the latter covers a more extended period in terms of weeks with three hours per day in the shop. And, of course, vocational-technical teachers must have adequate experience to qualify under the federal acts, which is not usually required in industrial arts, although desirable and exacted in many schools for teaching in upper levels of high school. The success of innovative programs of industrial arts can be more certainly determined by analyzing the activities proposed in a composite offering.

The analysis technique has brought genuineness and reality into industrial arts. Years ago, John Dewey said in his Kappa Delta Pi lectures, "Nothing can be more absurd educationally than to make a plea for a variety of active occupations in the school while decrying the need for progressive organization of information and ideas. Intelligent activity is distinguished from aimless activity by the fact that it involves selection of means—analysis—out of a variety of conditions that are present, and arrangement—synthesis—to reach an intended aim or purpose. . . . The final justification of shops, kitchen, and so on in the school is not just that they afford opportunity for activity, but that they provide the *kind* of activity for acquisition of mechanical skills which leads students to attend to the relation of means and ends, and then to consideration of the way things interact with one another to produce definite effects."[2] Dewey's words are a plea that we employ analysis in bringing about system and organization in our offerings if we are to match outside world experiences in our teaching.

Analysis Is Practical

If advanced industrial arts is to have technical-education value, its course content should be chosen from an analysis of a technical activity. The analysis technique, and perhaps it might well be called *activity analysis* in industrial arts, is an important means of connecting industrial arts with world achievement, of making industrial arts practical and thus giving it salable value. It is a step away from puttering, which is so often characteristic of industrial arts in the early years of schooling.

Industrial arts in the advanced levels of high school should be taught so that students who participate for a year or more can be assured of possession of salable abilities, even though they may advance to higher education and to professions. Part time work is often available to students with salable abilities. Industrial arts in the upper levels should have technical education value. The analysis technique, therefore, should be used to determine what to teach. The analysis technique should be taught to in- dustrial-arts teachers so they can understand what it is and can use it to proper advantage. It is a means to an end, and a very worthy end.

Analysis Makes Shop Teaching Realistic

When psychologists refer to the changing of behavior patterns through a learning situation, the patterns desired must be known. The patterns desired are not ethereal or psychic, nor should they be camouflaged in multiple-syllable words to confuse the student or to appear impressive. The patterns desired must be functional, practical. The various shops in industrial arts therefore must not be different from shops elsewhere. Operations in industrial arts

2. John Dewey, *Experience and Education* (New York: The Macmillan Co., 1938).

are not performed differently because they are performed in industrial arts.

Instruction must be provided. Demonstrations must be given and a variety of other means of teaching must be used as necessary. And what must the demonstrations include? The demonstrations must include such genuine things as the operations of the world of work outside of school; for example, in machine shop, the teacher must demonstrate how to *start and stop the lathe, lay out centers for cylindrical turning, mount work in the lathe,* and so on, depending upon the area of industry to be included. These skills are taught—and they must be taught for a good many obvious reasons, among them being training in safe work practices. There must be specific instruction, whether in traditional industrial arts or in innovative programs, and of course, objectives, management, evaluation, and other professional principles and practices are taken into account.

The Project Is a Vehicle of Instruction

Projects of some kind are basic, and likely will be so for many years to come. Production is industry, industry is production; therefore the project should remain important as an educational device. It lends itself to a visible and logical approach to instruction in problem-solving. Use of the project is emulated by other areas, which attests to the respect paid it.

Personal projects, group projects utilizing factory production methods, including personnel organization, management, and inspection procedures, enrich the educational values at all levels of high school. There need not be a fixed rule of choice; but whatever the projects, let there be worldlike subject matter. For some students a shop course may lend itself to greater emphasis on related information as against skills. Individual differences and community interests are also factors to take into account. Industrial arts offers generous opportunity for variety and enrichment of educational opportunity relating to industry. Whatever the content, it should be realistic, and it should be up to date. Analysis used as a curriculum research device makes this the more certain.

There must be instruction on related information,[3] although such instruction may be identified by other names, including

3. Chapter 5.

knowledge of science, mathematics, history, economics, and other academic subjects. And let us not overlook guidance information, which is so valuable in industrial arts. Unless the units taught are identical with the procedures of industry or the craft, they will have little guidance value.

And during learning, what is happening in the life of the learner? His behavior patterns are changing. Therefore, the instructional content must be genuine, not just words and expressions that represent nothing close to the world of work and merely enable the writer to "use words" to give an impression of scholarship.

How do we determine the desired content by means of which behavior patterns are changed? The answer is, by analyzing the work in question to determine its essential elements. The things that actually occur in the activity must be identified and placed in a body of resource materials, from which one draws ideas for developing a course of study. Chapter 10 tells the story of course development and its relation to analysis. You may wish to read that chapter before studying the analysis technique.

Analysis is necessary in all kinds of work, and certainly in the preparation of teachers. As was stated earlier in this chapter, analysis is a curricular research technique especially valuable in vocational-technical education and industrial arts. Those who have had doubts about the use of analysis in selection of subject matter in industrial arts have come to recognize its importance, especially since they have embraced technological terminology. Use and knowledge of this terminology is commercially salable, especially for students in the upper levels of high school. The use of analysis is of value in earning a living or in seeking advancement through higher education.

It was through the analysis technique that the instructional content now used by good teachers was derived. Any teacher attempting to do without such course materials is likely to be keeping a shop, not teaching it.

In New Programs

For those who are undertaking new types of programs by way of experimentation, the analysis technique should be used in determining and identifying current practices in industrial organization, production, and distribution. As a research technique it is exceedingly useful in keeping all aspects of instruction up-to-date. However, one must understand the analysis technique and know how to use it.

Summary

The making of an analysis of an occupation can be compared to the making of an inventory of a store. Just as a list is made of all the goods in the store, so a list is made of all the teaching units of the occupation. The instructional units thus obtained can be used for training purposes in school or out of school. Whatever system of analysis is used, it must be simple and readily understood by those who wish to use it.

The occupational analysis technique is necessary in the training of industrial and technical training personnel. The occupational elements become habits, and habits are not noticeable to those who have them; therefore it is necessary to analyze the occupation and list the elements so the new instructor will know what to teach. Experienced teachers also gain much from reanalyzing their work from time to time to keep it up-to-date.

The term *job analysis* has become a catchword in many areas of world activity. It has been misused in attempts to identify activities that are not of an analytical nature. While this analysis technique can be used in analyzing other than industrial occupations, it is designed for identifying instructional units for production purposes, rather than for personnel management.

The analysis technique helps to put system into the teaching of occupations and many other activities. In order to study the analysis procedure in its application to technical training, it is necessary first to make sure that the workers in industry are understood both as to work assignments and to terms used to identify them. Certain terminology also applies to the analysis technique itself. A major consideration is the development of ability to distinguish the elements of an industrial occupation from the jobs in which they are applied.

The training of vocational-technical teachers goes far beyond the making of the analysis. There remains the need for the study of learning and teaching, for course development, and for other phases of instructional procedures.

Analysis is used in selection and organization of subject matter in successful industrial arts programs and in research related to new experimental programs.

ASSIGNMENTS AND DISCUSSION TOPICS

1. List a few habits that you must develop in your occupation and discuss them in class.
2. Have you ever read or have you ever been told that industrial training is becoming less and less necessary because of the machine and automation? What is your belief? Do such statements mean that training procedures should be improved?
3. How can technical education keep up with changes in occupations?
4. What part do system and order play in attaining simplicity of organization when planning for growth and achievement?
5. Name several occupations having elements in them that can be compared to fundamental elements of arithmetic. Name some assignments that can be compared to problems in arithmetic and in which elements must be brought into use to get the assignment done.
6. Tell how you would teach a lesson in shopwork.
7. Discuss industrial arts in the senior high school in relation to technical usefulness directly after graduation or while attending college.

FOR FURTHER READING

Allen, C. R., *The Instructor, the Man, and the Job* (Philadelphia: J. B. Lippincott Co., 1919), Chaps. 1 and 2.

American Association of School Administrators, 25th Yearbook, *Schools for a New World* (Washington, D.C.: N.E.A., 1947).

Benjamin, Harold, *Man, The Problem Solver* (New York: Houghton Mifflin Co., 1930).

Bureau of Labor Statistics, *Occupational Outlook Handbook*. Washington, D.C.: United States Government Printing Office (1968–69), Bulletin No. 1550, 763 pages.

Dewey, John, *Experience and Education* (New York: The Macmillan Co., 1938).

Eddy, J. R. D., "T and I in the 60s," *American Vocational Journal*, Vol. 35, No. 4, April, 1960, pp. 10–11, 29.

Educational Policies Commission, *Education for All American Youth: A Further Look* (Washington, D.C.: N.E.A., 1952).

Feier, John L., editorial. "The Future of Innovative Programs in Industrial Arts," *IAVE Magazine*, Vol. 58, No. 10, December, 1969, p. 19.

Fryklund, Verne C., "Automation in Transition," *Industrial Arts and Vocational Education*, Vol. 56, No. 4, April, 1967, pp. 28–29, 90.

Great Cities Program for School Improvement, "Vocational Education in Preparation for the 'World of Work,'" *School Shop*, Vol. 19, No. 2, October, 1959, pp. 20–21, 84–90.

Krug, E. A., *The Secondary School Curriculum* (New York: Harper and Brothers, 1960).

Manpower, Challenge of the 1960s. (Washington, D.C.: U. S. Department of Labor, 1960).

Nelson, Howard F., "Industrial Arts Malnutrition—and a Prescription," *School Shop*, Vol. 28, No. 1, September, 1968, pp. 45–47, 85.

Norton, T. L., *Education for Work*, New York Regents Inquiry (New York: McGraw-Hill Book Co., 1938), Chap. 10.

Prosser, C. A., and Quigley, T. H., *Vocational Education in a Democracy* (Chicago: American Technical Society, 1949).

Rose, Homer C., *Development and Supervision of Training Programs* (Chicago: American Technical Society, 1964).

"Roundtable: Comparing Programs in Industrial Education," *IAVE Magazine*, Vol. 59, No. 1, January, 1970, pp. 24 ff.

Schuchat, Theor, "The Vocational Education Act of 1963," *School Shop*, Vol. 23, No. 8, April, 1964, pp. 30–34.

Selvidge, R. W., *How to Teach a Trade* (Peoria: C. A. Bennett Co., 1923), Chaps. 1, 2, and 3.

Selvidge, R. W., and Fryklund, V. C., *Principles of Trade and Industrial Teaching* (Peoria: C. A. Bennett Co., 1946), Chaps. 1, 2, and 3.

Silvius, G. H., and Bohn, R. C., *Organizing Course Materials* (Bloomington, Ill.: McKnight and McKnight Publishing Co., 1961), Chap. 4.

Silvius, G. H., and Curry, E. H., *Teaching Successfully* (Bloomington, Ill.: McKnight and McKnight Publishing Co., 1967).

Struck, F. T., *Vocational Education for a Changing World* (New York: John Wiley and Sons, Inc., 1944).

Modern Industrial Workers

The purpose of this chapter is to describe typical workers in industry and to discuss their work, their outlook for future employment, and certain important terms relating to them and of importance to education. The interpretations presented here are based on studies and experiences involving industrial practices and writings in industrial education, science, sociology, and economics.

Education and Industry

The educator who may be in doubt about the relation of education to the problem of mass production and automation in industry would profit much by a study of industry in the community. Indeed, such a study would reveal much that would be helpful in vitalizing education. There is much to be learned in industry that would be of value in modernizing education, in making school achievement at least parallel to community achievement and not lagging behind it. Certainly included in the preparation of the administrator of the general school should be a systematic intensive study of industry. There he would find much valuable content for academic instruction as well as encouragement of education for industry. There he would find that while occupations change, they are not wholly lost. Furthermore, he would find that old occupations are influenced by new processes and inventions, and that new occupations are appearing. He would also find that continuous education of all kinds is needed in order that people who must work can prepare for it and keep up with the vast changes that are taking place in occupations.

During the past several years, the author has studied the want-ad sections of the Sunday editions of metropolitan newspapers throughout the United States, and has observed the ongoing demand for skilled workers in major occupational areas represented in training programs in technical schools and upper levels of high schools. These include machine shop, drafting, sheet metalworking, electronics, auto mechanics, building construction occupations, business machine repair, plumbing, graphic arts, and many variations of the foregoing, despite the growing use of computers and numerical control. There are increasing opportunities in the latter areas also and want-ads seeking trainees are many.

In Figure 1 is shown information relating to the outlook for employment in the major occupational areas garnered from the Occupational Outlook Handbook, Bulletin 1550, United States Department of Labor. This does not include the great number of occupations in aeronautical and space work involving the skilled workers represented in the table. There are tens of thousands of mechanics and technicians employed in these industries with a minimum of 20,000 to 30,000 replacements annually.

Scientific development has been compounding through the centuries. One discovery and creation has led to still another. Yet certain basic occupations form the means of production and maintenance of the many new gadgets. The crafts do not always produce in exactly the same way as always because mechanical

Fig. 1
Outlook for Technical Occupations*

Occupation	Estimate of Number Employed Early in 1967	Estimate of Minimum Number Needed in 1970s (New Jobs and Replacements)
Machinists	400,000	84,000
Electricians	1,156,000	222,000
Tool and Die	150,000	36,000
Foundrymen	400,000	108,000
Patternmakers	18,000	4,800
Welders	460,000	84,000
Draftsmen	270,000	10,000
Sheet Metal	55,000	9,600
Auto Mechanics	580,000	103,000
Auto Body Mechanics	97,000	18,000
Bricklayers	175,000	33,000
Cement Masons	750,000	156,000
Carpenters	850,000	240,000
Plumbers	350,000	84,000
Appliance Repair	200,000	90,000
TV and Radio Repair	125,000	16,800
Graphic Arts	365,000	72,000
Business Machine Repair	80,000	80,000

* *Occupational Outlook Handbook*, U.S. Bureau of Labor Statistics, Bulletin No. 1550 (1968–69), Washington, D.C.: United States Government Printing Office.

devices have improved the efficiency of workers, but the basic skills and know-how of the occupations are still present. Mathematics has not changed fundamentally, but certain mechanical equipment has made the mathematician more efficient.

Something is produced and maintained regardless of the origin of the idea for the gadget in question. Even though it may be an automatic machine such as a computer; the machine still must be produced and maintained. Another automatic machine may share in this production, yet someone must produce the auxiliary equipment and maintain it. Training and retraining are ongoing needs.

Unfortunately, many people believe that most modern industrial workers need very little training. The work is assumed to be so highly specialized and automatic that training is not necessary. Consequently, there is doubt of the value of practical content that could be useful in academic classes, and youth are frequently discouraged by counselors from enrolling in technical classes. It is said that there is a diminishing need for vocational and technical education, yet the world is so constituted that an academic education alone is of little value in the important personal responsibility of earning a living. There is daily proof of this in employment offices when untrained persons seek employment. The individual who cannot claim occupational usefulness has little chance in his plea for a job. Moreover, a college degree is of limited value as an employment asset if it does not include some kind of occupational preparation.

Most industries are not automatic, but all industries, whether they are automatic or not, require highly skilled workers to produce and to maintain equipment. They will continue to need them for many years to come. These are the many workers who have been and still are involved in the processing of raw materials into finished goods and in the maintenance of the finished products. There will be modification, training, and retraining, but manpower with skill and intelligence will continue to be the productive mainstay of industry.

Modern Industrial Workers

The analysis technique for instructors is an exceedingly useful curriculum research technique in the study of activities in the work areas of a community. Analysis would be of doubtful value, however, if the terminology associated with it were confusing and consequently improperly used. The conditions of industry could better be understood, especially in relation to training needs and curriculum enrichment, if the terminology employed were common to all educators, not just to those who are concerned with technical education. Personnel workers also could gain much by unifying their references to workers in industry.

The author, in connection with employment studies in more

than fifty factories in the Minneapolis-St. Paul area, found that the terms used in reference to workers varied in different factories and in different departments of the same factory. The casual designations of the workers, as well as of their duties, and the abilities ascribed to them were found to vary among all the people who were interested in industrial conditions at the time.

Not only is there variation in daily practice in terms of referring to workers, but books and magazine articles do not show agreement. Many writers who are not familiar with industry do not understand with sufficient clearness the work performed. What constitutes a "trade" as compared to specialized industrial work should be understood by anyone who attempts discussion of industrial problems and by anyone who is interested in training. The terms that will be discussed here have value (1) in clarifying the duties of workers as a basis for understanding certain practices in technical education and (2) in learning the analysis technique for occupations.

Skilled Mechanics in Industry

Among engineers, the term "skilled mechanic" represents the highest type of workman, whether in production industry or in a custom technical occupation. To qualify for the title, a skilled mechanic must be able to do any of the work that is required of workers in a particular industrial activity; he is a technologist. He must be able to perform practically all the operations and be in command of all scientific facts, be able to read drawings, and make calculations that may be essential to the performance of his work. The skilled mechanic can carry out any new assignment in his activity, plan carefully and quickly how it is to be done, and then do it. His work can properly be compared to the solving of problems in mathematics. One who solves a mathematical problem must know and be able to use the necessary operations in mathematics. We may think of these operations as essential elements. When a new problem confronts him, he must quickly perceive the operations or elements necessary to solve the problem and put them into proper combination, step by step, to obtain the correct answer. A skilled mechanic must quickly be able to survey a given situation as does a problem solver in mathematics, plan the proper combination of elements, and carry out the assignment properly. Elements are present in both operations, but technical problems involve materials and ideas whereas mathematical solutions involve ideas only. The assignment of the skilled mechanic usually covers a much longer time for completion than does the assignment of the mathematician.

The skilled mechanic is the craftsman who is associated in the history of industry with the time before mass methods became the major means of production and a given article was produced practically in its entirety by one man. Little by little, because of competition and demands for goods, the work assignments in making an article were distributed among several persons who became specialists or operatives. Where once a table was produced entirely by a master craftsman, later several men took part in producing such a table. One person became a specialist in producing table legs, another in finishing, and so on.

While the story of the growth of competitive methods and of meeting the increasing demands of people for goods, and the resulting changes in work assignments, is exceedingly interesting, it need not be discussed here. However, mass-production methods and automation have not eliminated the skilled mechanic. The work has changed, to be sure, because of improved means of getting the work done by machines and by more scientific methods, but the skilled mechanic has not been eliminated from industrial production in this nuclear age (see Figure 1). He is needed more than ever and must continue to be exacting in his work. Persons who can perform many operations and who possess knowledge necessary for doing complicated work assignments are still needed in large numbers in industry and in the great mass of service and small shop occupations. While the machine and automation have increased the need for skilled mechanics, many new kinds of mechanics have appeared because of the great expansion in kinds of products. Those who understand the world of work know this. The percentage of change in employment during the past decade, 1960–70 (Figure 2), reveals that the need for skilled and semi-skilled workers is growing. Training and retraining must be continuous in order that the abilities of workers will match the requirements of changing technology.

Following is a brief list of typical skilled mechanics in metal production. There are many more in this and in other industries.

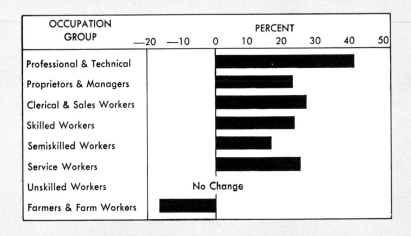

Fig. 2. *Percent change in employment, 1960–70.*[1]

Machinists	Welders	Boilermakers
Sheet-Metalworkers	Plumbers	Millwrights
Patternmakers	Draftsmen	Blacksmiths
Tool and Diemakers	Setup Men	Molders
Electricians	Steam Fitters	Bronze Chasers

Skilled mechanics today do not always do all the work on a given article. For example, the patternmaker makes the pattern for an article, the molder molds it, the foundryman casts it, and the machinist does the final finishing. Each of the persons involved is a skilled mechanic. He performs all the work on the article that is characteristic of his occupation. The skilled mechanic may also be thought of as a custom worker. That is, he must be able to do all the work of his occupation, even though he may not complete any given article. He must be a versatile worker.

1. From *Manpower, Challenge of the 1960s* (Washington, D. C.: U. S. Department of Labor, 1960).

The type of producer comparable to the skilled mechanic need not be thought of as one whose work is in industry and who must work in metal or wood. The tailor, baker, signwriter, upholsterer, printer, and hundreds of other workers whose duties are largely of custom nature, are in the category of skilled mechanics. The tailer may be classed as a skilled mechanic, and his work must be analyzed into its elements if it is to be taught. We think of him more generally, however, as a craftsman. But, of course, craftsmen and skilled mechanics are in the same occupational class.

Another group of skilled mechanics is increasing in number, and training must be provided for them. They are service mechanics who repair watches, refrigerators, automobiles, radios, phonographs, television sets, and who make installations. Their work is to discover or diagnose trouble in a machine and repair it for further use. They are problem solvers as are mechanics in custom trades. They do not produce articles, they service them. Like mechanics in custom trades, they must have a variety of skills and technological knowledge of the occupation that must be drawn upon in order to locate and correct a difficulty in a machine.

Operatives in Industry

There should now be little question as to the meaning of the terms and nature of the work performed by skilled mechanics. The exact nature of the work of the operative will be considered now. It should not be necessary to go into the details of the conditions that led to the existence of operatives in industry. It has been mentioned that the breaking down of the work of the craftsman of old, in consequence of methods of mass production, covers the history of the rise of the workers that we call operatives. Whereas the skilled mechanic can perform practically all the operations, and knows the scientific facts and other information necessary in the occupation, the operative can perform only one or a few operations at the most, and knows little if any information of the kind required of the skilled mechanic. He is also called a semiskilled worker. His responsibilities are limited.

Usually, every step performed by an operative has been so planned that all details are listed in a set and required order of performance. The number of duties that he performs on a given article is limited; the order is carefully determined and rigid; and repetition is so frequent that there is practically automatic performance. From day to day, week to week, and month to month a given operation is repeatedly performed. As the production continues, the semiskilled worker's job is but a single step, or a few at the most, in the making of an article. This work may be the operation of a machine for coiling bed springs, the assembly of stepladders, or any other of a multitude of operations in manufacture.

While each operation will require some degree of special skill, at no time will the duties of an operative include the entire range of duties of a skilled mechanic. Little responsibility is required of an operative compared to that needed in a skilled technical occupation where complex judgments are necessary. An operative may be able to perform many operations in a factory; he may be versatile, yet he may fall far short of being a skilled mechanic. There may be few situations which require much thought or necessity for judgment even for a versatile operative.

The following brief descriptions of duties should further clarify the meaning of the term and the duties of operation. The list is taken at random without reference to any particular factory.

ASSEMBLERS, FINAL. These workers do repetitive fitting and assembling of various units of a product. For instance, in a factory that builds motors, they place motors in frames, connect terminal leads to binding posts, attach switches, and bolt the end shields to enclose the motor. Should this be custom rather than repetitive work, it is not semiskilled but falls into the class of work performed by the skilled mechanic.

ASSEMBLERS, SUB. These workers fit and assemble minor parts to form units that are later assembled by final assemblers. In the factory just mentioned, subassemblers would attach small parts, such as commutators, brushes, and solder terminals.

BORING-MILL HANDS OR OPERATIVES. This is essentially a machine-shop occupation and a high type of semiskilled work. It also may be classed as the work of a skilled mechanic when it ceases to be repetitive. The worker runs either a vertical machine called a boring mill or a horizontal boring machine.

CHIPPERS. A foundry job. Projecting parts left in the casting process must be removed with a hammer, cold chisel, or pneumatic chisel. It is not a high type of semiskilled work.

DRILL-PRESS OPERATIVES. Operate gang drills, radial drills, or other types of drill presses to drill, countersink, and tap holes in parts. It is a common factory operation which requires limited training.

GRINDING-MACHINE OPERATIVES. Operate machines that give a fine finish to surfaces.

INSPECTORS AND TESTERS. Common to most factories. Inspect raw materials, parts, units, and finished products.

LATHE OPERATIVES. Operate engine and turret lathes; essentially a machine-shop operation. It is semiskilled when the work is highly repetitive.

MACHINE OPERATIVES, GENERAL. Operatives of general machine tools of minor classification.

MILLING-MACHINE HANDS AND OPERATIVES. Operate various types of milling machines.

Skilled Mechanics and Operatives Work Together

On first observation, it is difficult for the lay person to tell the difference between a skilled mechanic and an operative. They may work together in a given plant. As stated earlier in this chapter, one needs to know industry thoroughly in order to pass judgments on the status of the workers. While skilled mechanics and operatives are described separately, there is no exact line of demarcation between them. The terms skilled mechanic and operative are convenient to use in order to set off two major classes of workers whose abilities seem to fuse into each other. Industrial workers vary in their abilities from zero to a very high degree.

In modern industry there is continuing change in the breakdown and in the creation of work units. The tendency is toward a simplification of the complicated work units and toward automation, but at the same time new developments and demands for new goods tend to create new kinds of workers, both operatives and skilled mechanics. The skilled mechanic performs duties that are of custom nature, sets up machine tools and instruments and reads drawings. His duties may be of service nature, in which he must be able to overhaul a machine completely. He requires much more training and experience to qualify for his work than does the operative. The operative's responsibility is limited to a rather small amount of planned performance, the planning having been done by someone else. His work is characterized mainly by the fact that it is repetitive. Complicated machines may be involved, but the fact that the work is repetitive in a limited area marks the workman as an operative. The more recent term *technician* is used to refer to workers possessing a gamut of abilities from high class repetitive work to highly scientific production work. The term is often used to refer to operatives as well as to skilled mechanics.

Abilities of Operatives in Industry

The abilities required in the performance of operative work include dexterity of hand manipulation, within a limited scope, and ability to form judgments concerning the few manipulative acts. Manipulative ability and judgment-forming ability do not run parallel with each other in equal amounts. An operative may require any amount from near zero to a very high degree of manipulative ability and may at the same time require any amount from near zero to a very high degree of judgment-forming ability. No two semiskilled workers need the same amount of skill. To illustrate, two commonly found types of operatives are workers on punch presses and on boring mills. They perform operations requiring extreme degrees, low and high, of ability. The punch-press operatives require less manipulative ability and need to form fewer judgments than do the boring mill operatives. The latter are regarded as being among the highest types of operatives. They require a high degree of manipulative ability and an even higher degree of judgment-forming ability to do their work.

As with skilled mechanics, operatives work in all industries. They are not necessarily confined to metalworking plants. Operatives work in garment production, tailoring, baking, candymaking, and so on. Both men and women are included in both classes of workers.

Training of Workers

The amounts of training required of workers vary as do abilities. It is difficult to state exactly the training time needed because of individual differences in learners as well as differences in requirements in various occupations. Skilled mechanics, under present facilities, can be trained in from two to seven years. Skilled mechanics such as fine instrument makers require a much longer training period than do the usual classes of machinists. Long experience in service as advanced apprentices is characteristic of the higher types of skilled mechanics. Furthermore, their training never ceases. They must continually study in order to keep up with technological advances.

The time required for training operatives varies from a few hours to several months. Some very light types of repetitive work can be learned quickly, while certain types of repetitive machine operations require several months of intensive training. In lathe operation, for example, a knowledge and practical application of a certain amount of related mathematics is essential, in addition to rather complex manipulative performance; there is an increase in learning time over that required for the more simple operations.

Service occupations employ large numbers of skilled mechanics such as electricians, radio and television experts, automobile specialists, and repairmen for the constantly increasing numbers of conveniences designed for human happiness and comfort. The small shop field includes the large number of small establishments that employ many skilled mechanics such as service experts, sheet-metalworkers, plumbers, cabinetmakers, machinists, and the like. All of these are increasing in numbers and all require extensive training. Whether the workers to be trained are operatives on repetitive jobs of complicated nature or skilled mechanics, the analysis technique is necessary to determine the essential elements that must be taught.

Training should be given workers according to the degree of manipulative ability and judgment forming required, rather than by classification according to technical or nontechnical groups. Training should be made available to all who need it, provided that such training is necessary and that it is for a *useful occupation*.

This would embrace any payroll job that calls for training in any area of useful work.

High types of repetitive work, if the work is generally of employable nature and if considerable instruction and time is required for learning, should therefore be included in a training program. This is practical and in keeping with the rapidly changing conditions of work in industry.

Persons who are entrusted by the public with the important responsibility of operating the schools efficiently in the interest of youth should know much about working conditions and opportunities in industry. Merely reading about them—frequently the literature is prepared by persons who view the conditions from a distance—does not reveal the true situation. Consequently, youth are told in the schools of the limitation of opportunities in industry while at the same time the production world outside of school demands occupational preparation of the youth who seek employment. Youth knows this and they say so. Moreover, they ask for training in technical pursuits. If education is to keep pace with world conditions, the training of educators should include the gathering of firsthand knowledge of community situations. This cannot be done successfully if those who attempt such study do so at a distance. It cannot be done if knowledge in books is limited to use within the four walls of a classroom. The place of application is in the world outside of school. Moreover, industry is the largest area of application for many of the things found in books, yet youth often are told that opportunity in industry is limited because of the nuclear age. Jobs are available and opportunities for advancement are many (see Figure 1). Let us learn about workers in industry; learn the status of these workers, what they do, what training they really need, and the opportunities available to youth in industry. Let there be opportunities to bring classroom education and education for industry together in a practical way.

Summary

Educators should study industry so they can be informed as to the work that is done, and as to the training that is needed by industrial workers. Much can be learned that would be helpful in making school achievement practical in academic as well as in shop classes. Much book learning has practical application in industry, but study of its applications is necessary so the school offerings will really be practical. Study of industry will also enlighten educators regarding opportunities for youth, and there are many despite, and even because of, automation. Youth should not be discouraged by counselors from entering vocational-technical training. Jobs are available for those who are trained.

The workers in industry are placed in two classes for convenience, namely, skilled mechanics and operatives. To qualify as a skilled mechanic, one must be able to do any of the work that is required in a particular industrial activity. He must be able to undertake any new assignment, plan carefully and quickly how it is to be done, and then do it. He is a problem solver. Skilled mechanics are on the increase and not on the decrease as is assumed by those who are uninformed. Study of industry would be enlightening on this point.

Workers in occupations other than industrial who may be classed with skilled mechanics are the tailor, baker, signwriter, upholsterer, printer, and so on. Any workers whose duties are of custom nature, or nonrepetitive, are classed as skilled mechanics or craftsmen. In order to train people to work in any of the many skilled occupations, it is necessary to make an inventory of the elements to be taught by means of the analysis technique. There are occupations also that involve repairing and overhauling of machines. They are called service occupations and the workers are service technicians.

Whereas the skilled mechanic can do any of the work in a highly skilled occupation, the operative can perform only one or a few limited assignments. He repeats the assignments day after day and thus makes his living. Most operatives need little training.

Skilled mechanics and operatives work together, and they are hard to distinguish by persons who do not know about the real conditions in industry. There is no dividing line that sets off one class of workers from another. Their abilities vary from a low degree to a high degree of manipulative and mental ability. Therefore the training needs vary. From two to seven years of training are required to qualify for the work of the skilled mechanic. A few hours to several months of training are required to qualify as an operative. According to a study reported, 44.3 percent of the workers in industry required training in order to qualify for their jobs.

A knowledge of industrial workers and the work they do should be studied firsthand so that youth can be rightfully informed and be given training when and if they ask for it.

ASSIGNMENTS AND DISCUSSION TOPICS

1. Compare the skilled mechanic and the operative.
2. Name several skilled occupations aside from those listed in this chapter. Also several repetitive jobs.
3. How can you learn about the opportunities for youth in industry in your community?
4. Name a skilled occupation that is completely lost because of mechanization, and explain the circumstances.
5. Name several occupations that you believe do not require training.
6. What must one know to judge the status of workers?
7. Name some skilled occupations that you know are necessary in the maintenance of hotels.
8. Name several assignments in your occupation that can be compared to solving problems in mathematics.
9. Review the help-wanted sections of the want ads in your metropolitan newspapers and discuss the needs for workers in the various skilled categories.

FOR FURTHER READING

American Association of School Administrators, 25th Yearbook, *Schools for a New World* (Washington, D.C.: N.E.A., 1947).

Benjamin, Harold, *Man, The Problem Solver* (New York: Houghton Mifflin Co., 1930).

Daffern, G. N., *Management Development in a Changing World* (New York: Simmons-Boardman Publishing Corporation, 1960), pp. 17–111.

Fryklund, Verne C., "Industrial Education in the Fifth Year of Our Space Age," *Industrial Arts and Vocational Education*, Vol. 51, No. 6, June, 1962, pp. 12, 13.

Kilbridge, M. D., "Non-productive Work as Factor in Economic Division of Labor," *Journal Industrial Engineering*, Vol. 12, No. 3, May–June, 1961, pp. 155–159.

Manpower, Challenge of the 60s (Washington, D.C.: U. S. Department of Labor, 1960).

Occupational Outlook Handbook, Bulletin 1550 (Washington, D.C.: U. S. Department of Labor, 1968–69).

Prosser, C. A., and Quigley, T. H., *Vocational Education in a Democracy* (Chicago: American Technical Society, 1949).

Pearce, Theodore, "Fluid Power—An Emerging Industrial Art," *School Shop*, Vol. 23, No. 9, May, 1964, pp. 20–21, 31.

Rudiger, E. R., "Teaching Motor Skills in Depth in Vocational Areas," *Industrial Arts and Vocational Education*, Vol. 54, No. 2, February, 1965, pp. 29, 30.

Other Kinds of Analysis

Occupational analysis should not be confused with job descriptions, job specifications, organization and flow charts that show relationships of personnel or routing of materials in an organization or plant, time and motion study, job classification techniques, analysis of mobility of workers, and machinery studies. Let us study briefly a few of these techniques in order that there can be an understanding of their place in the world of work, and in order that they will not be confused in the minds of persons who are interested in technical education. Many people, outside of industrial education, assume that these techniques are useful for job-training purposes, and because they have attempted to use them for that purpose and have had limited success they have assumed that analysis is not helpful. Workers in technical education should know about them and be able to make the distinctions.

Job Descriptions

Job descriptions include statements relating to general duties, training required, working conditions, remuneration, and so on, of any person who would attempt to qualify as a worker in a particular occupation. This technique is also called occupational description. It does not include the detailed fundamentals necessary for training as does analysis for instructional purposes. Job descriptions are general in nature, and are used in personnel work, in employment offices, and in vocational guidance. They frequently are used before making an analysis for training in order to describe properly the occupation to be analyzed. As a rule, however, it is unnecessary to make the preliminary job description because the mechanic teacher whose work is being analyzed and the analyst usually know what they are analyzing. Little general description is needed. The actual analysis to determine instructional units requires all the time that can be devoted to it. Job descriptions are frequently referred to as job analysis under the assumption that they are adequate for training purposes. Job descriptions are more valuable for hiring than for training. On pages 35 and 36 is a typical job description assumed by many personnel and guidance workers to be an analysis for job training, but it has limited value in training.

Every industry and business employing persons who must perform varied kinds of work should have job descriptions of all assignments for effective personnel placement and accounting.

Included in each description should be a general statement of duties, training required in order to qualify, location of the assignment in a department, mental and physical effort involved, responsibility for tools and equipment, safety factors, health conditions, promotional features, wage brackets, labor relations aspects, and any other items necessary to assure employment of the best possible personnel for the job at hand.

Some industries make rather thorough analyses of the duties involved in each job. It is not unusual for labor organizations to require very complete job descriptions in setting forth requirements for apprentices. Instructional units often are listed.

Although the personnel worker who prepares job descriptions need not be an expert in occupational analysis, a study of this

FORD MOTOR COMPANY

JOB DESCRIPTION

PLANT OF LOCATION

JOB TITLE: Electrician   PAY GRADE: CODE   NO. 1001
TOTAL POINTS: DATE:

GENERAL DESCRIPTION OF DUTIES

Installs, repairs, tests and maintains electrical equipment and fixtures.

Determines method and sequence of proposed installation of electrical fixtures and equipment such as motors, control panels, switches and transformers by referring to blueprints, schematic drawings, specifications or verbal instructions. Assembles and installs switch boxes, conduit lines, wiring systems, panels and related equipment, using tradesman's tools. Routes conduit lines and pulls wire through conduit by means of fish tape. Connects one end of wire to electrical equipment and splices other end to source of power. Occasionally cuts or bores through walls, ceilings or partitions, using saws and chisels. Analyzes failures of electrical equipment, using ammeter, voltmeter, ohmmeter, drawings and visual inspection. Dismantles and repairs equipment by cleaning contact points with sandpaper, replacing defective wires, motor brushes, condensers and burned out fuses, using electrician's hand tools. Reassembles and installs repaired units. Tests continuity of electrical circuit in installed or repaired equipment, using electrical measuring instruments. Performs preventative maintenance activities, such as making periodic visual inspections and taping frayed or exposed wires, cleaning and oiling motors and securing loose connections. Performs repairs on electronically controlled equipment, such as gauges, testing machines and speed devices, by testing and replacing defective tubes, resistors, capacitators and related parts.

(Over)

JOB TITLE: Electrician

PLANT OR LOCATION:

CODE NO. 1001

PAY GRADE:

	DEGREE	POINTS
1. EDUCATIONAL BACKGROUND. Equivalent to a four year apprenticeship covering principles of electrical construction, maintenance and repair, involving thorough knowledge of shop mathematics, electrical theory, wiring, generators, motors, transformers, electrical circuits and welding controls, and fundamentals of electronics.	E	
2. JOB TRAINING. 13 months through 24 months required to become acquainted with various types of electrical equipment and to be able to analyze cause of failures and make necessary repairs to electrical equipment.	E	
3. MENTAL OR VISUAL EFFORT. Requires concentrated mental and visual attention to lay out and perform installation and maintenance functions. Analyzes faulty operation of electrical equipment and makes necessary repairs.	D	
4. PHYSICAL EFFORT. Moderate physical exertion. Occasionally works from ladders and scaffolds and in awkward position. Uses light and medium weight hand tools and hand power tools. Occasionally handles heavy equipment such as conduit, electric motors and coils of wire.	C	
5. RESPONSIBILITY FOR MATERIAL OR PRODUCT. Exercises considerable care and attention in making installations and repairs to prevent damage which would necessitate removal or rework of equipment. **ESTIMATED COST:**	C $100	
6. RESPONSIBILITY FOR TOOLS AND EQUIPMENT. Exercises ordinary care to prevent damage to hand power tools, measuring instruments, drill presses and simple machinery such as pipe cutting and threading machines. **ESTIMATED COST:**	B Inter.	
7. RESPONSIBILITY FOR SAFETY OF OTHERS. Requires sustained high degree of care to prevent injuries to others while controlling flow of electric power. Required to post danger signs or to guard switch boxes.	D	
8. WORK SURROUNDINGS. Exposed to considerable accumulations of dust and grease on electrical equipment. Exposed to considerable smoke, heat and fumes when working near furnaces. Works inside and outside.	C	
9. UNAVOIDABLE HAZARDS. Exposed to serious injury while working on high voltage electricity or to falls while working on high scaffolds, roofs and structures.	D	
TOTAL POINTS		

technique is certainly helpful to him in preparing accurate listings of the many duties to be performed in any job. He is then better able to differentiate the manipulative skills from the mental skills and to describe the duties accordingly.

Personnel workers often do not sufficiently understand the nature of training content. Familiarizing such workers with the occupational analysis technique is very useful.

Job Specifications

Job specifications are used in connection with production. Statements are written concerning material, finish, cost, quantity, and so on, of the product to be made and delivered. For example, the printer writes the specifications for 1,000 copies of a program to be printed. There would be included such information as kind, size, and weight of paper, type, cuts, borders, style, inks, layout, and so on. This information usually is placed on the outside of a special envelope in which the layout and proofs will be kept. In many productive situations in other occupations, similar specifications are necessary. Drawings are included with job specifications. Job specifications are sometimes carelessly referred to as job descriptions.

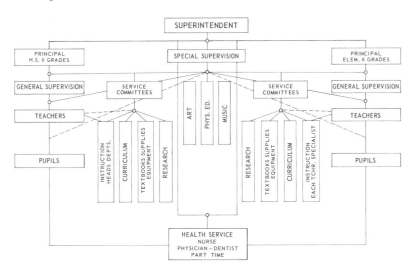

Fig. 3. *Organization of school supervision in a small city.*

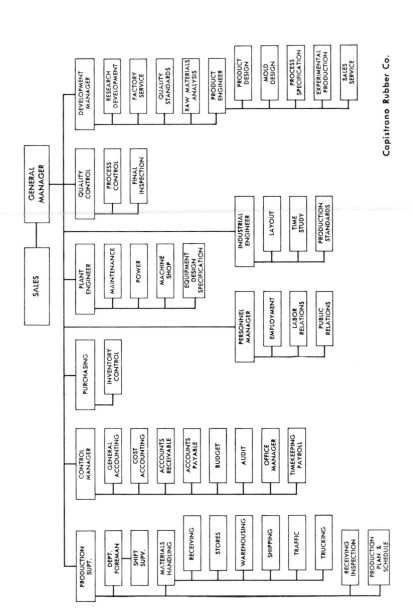

Fig. 4. *Plant organization chart.*

Organization Charts

Organization charts show relationships of personnel or services in an organization. Figure 3, which shows the organization of school supervision in a small city, and Figure 4, which shows the organization of a large manufacturing plant, are typical organization charts. Charts such as these are helpful in counseling, though there is limited use for them in analyzing an occupation.

Flow Charts

Flow charts show the station to station or department to department progress of material or a product in a plant. Engineers in industrial management have considerable need for such charts (Figure 5).[1] This type of work should not be confused with the analysis of an occupation for training purposes, although it may be used prior to or simultaneously with such analysis to show relationships to material and personnel organization or to show the place of an occupation in an economic area. It has vocational guidance value and may be used in counseling. Such charts have some value in the training of teachers for, and learners of, an occupation or production job.

Time and Motion Study

Time and motion study techniques are often assumed to be for training of teachers of an occupation. These techniques represent a form of research for gathering facts that will be of value in reducing production costs and in setting up wage incentive plans.

Time study includes the observation of operations and the timing of the essential steps to gather data that can be used in determining job time standards in production. Figure 6 shows the scope of time and motion study in graph form.[2] Motion study involves the observation of an operation to determine the quickest way to perform it. Both techniques are in use by efficiency engineers in production plants throughout the world.

1. R. R. Mayer, *Production Management* (New York: McGraw-Hill Book Co., 1962), p. 23.
2. R. M. Barnes, *Motion and Time Study* (New York: John Wiley and Sons, 1963), p. 7.

There are different systems of wage-incentive plans in which time and motion-study techniques are in use, and a few of the names associated with them are Bedaux, Diemer, Emerson, Gantt, Halsey, Haynes, and Taylor.

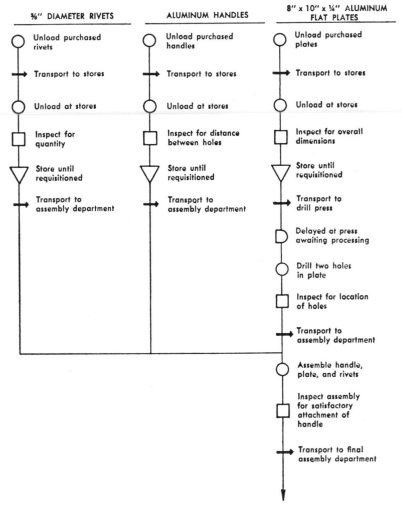

Fig. 5. *A material flow process chart for a sliding door assembly.*

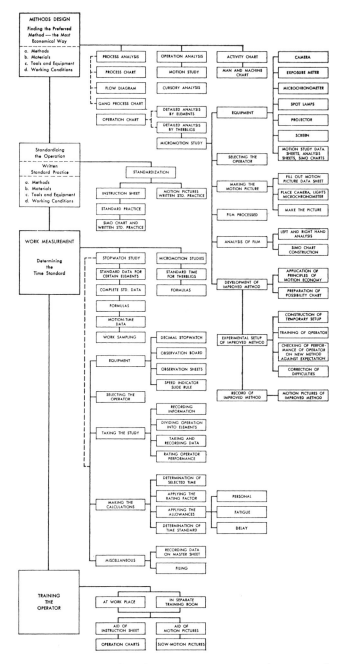

Fig. 6. *Tools and techniques of motion and time study.*

Job Classification

Job classification is another engineering procedure that frequently is thought of as an analysis technique for use by instructors of an occupation. This technique is used in establishing base rates for classifying all jobs in a business. Job classification is of two kinds: classification (1) by occupations and (2) by grades within an occupation or in several occupations.

Job classification is used as a first step in establishing base rates in production. The first kind assumes classification by occupation only, as, for example, sheet metalworkers, plumbers, truckers, and so on. The second kind assumes classification by abilities involved in doing jobs in a number of occupations. Workers could be classified in most industries as A, B, C, D, and E workers according to the training, job intelligence, and skill required. Class A would represent the highest class and E the lowest. This type of job classification is used in attempts to develop a uniform pay basis for workers in accordance with their abilities. High and low abilities are required of workers within an occupation and pay, it is argued, should be determined accordingly. These techniques should not be confused with occupational analysis for training workers.

Analysis of Mobility and Obsolescence

Study of movements of workers from one plant to another or from one city to another, and from operative jobs in one occupation to operative jobs in other occupations, in attempts to learn working conditions and the like, is involved in the problem of mobility. Study of machines in relation to age, production capacity, safety and ease of handling, production competition, and displacement of workers is involved in the problem of obsolescence.

The kinds of analysis just mentioned are only a few of the many research techniques relating to personnel work and production. Some of them may be wisely used for orientation purposes under some conditions in connection with the training of workers, but none of them should be identified with the kind of analysis intended for training purposes, nor do they represent any major part of the procedure.

The techniques employed in these procedures are helpful to engineers and plant managers in connection with production, but they have little value to the person who desires to discover the instructional units to be taught to a learner in a given trade. Certain fundamental units for training must be discovered and the occupational analysis technique should be used to discover them. Such an analysis is fact finding for instructional purposes and it is an important curriculum research technique for technical education.

SYSTEMS ANALYSIS[3]

The term *systems analysis* is often used with vague meaning to suggest a new approach, something different and up-to-date in educational procedure. However, it is a relatively recent research technique in business and industry conceived for the solution of problems relating to identifying and overcoming difficulties in effective utilization of resources in management, production and distribution of goods. It is the grand strategy of management for overall planning, and in the process, the existing or potential problems of management, production and distribution are assumed to be identified and solved. The term is also used in a limited way in connection with computer planning and programming.

There seems not to be full agreement regarding the technique of systems analysis suited to the study of the many kinds of industry and business because of the innumerable variables involved, human and mechanical. There are as many variables as there are people and human effort, and the unclear reference to the systems approach increases the variables and often ends up with an unsolved problem. The phenomenon of individual differences is ongoing and human intuition is as variable as the number of people involved.

Terminology

There are several unique terms in systems analysis and among them are *simulation, tradeoff, feedback* and *alternative.* Simulated presentations are models for use in general planning. They are assumed to represent the desired outcome in layout and personnel management and in presentation of lessons. There is some disagreement among business executives as to the value of simulated layouts. They do have some value under conditions typical of the offering being simulated and when potential danger is involved.

3. Verne C. Fryklund, "What is Systems Analysis?" *IAVE Magazine*, Vol. 59, No. 4, April, 1970, p. 33.

Examples are the Driver Training Devices, Link Trainer in the Air Force, the Diesel Train Simulator of the Santa Fe Railroad and the NASA Gemini Training Devices. These were not associated initially with systems analysis though they represent situations in which extra care must be taken for the safety of the persons in training, and they reduce the time and cost of training.

Simulation may be the layout of equipment with models. However, in an ongoing program in an established facility, simulation may be of doubtful value. It can be a hindrance to learning and it should not be used in order to appear erudite and modern.

There are so many variables in plant management, as earlier stated, that simulation may become confusion. If the variables are few and of mechanical nature, objectivity is possible and simulation is therefore helpful. The layout of a plant in terms of known and proved production procedures and sequences is such a possibility. The planning of laboratories with models is illustrative of application in education. But let us not simulate in the actual classroom or prepare for instructional content by simulating. At the operating level where planned instruction takes place, simulation is unproductive of genuine learning. It can then be only one thing— an exercise. We have long ago determined that use of exercises in the laboratory is unwise when specific instruction is under way, and when the instructional content of a recognized industrial or business activity has been objectively listed.

Tradeoff, feedback and *alternative* are the other terms used by persons who experiment with systems analysis. Essentially, it is trial and error, "Try this" since it seems proper under the circumstances, but in feedback it may prove not to be a success. Then try an alternative—tradeoff. Feedback is checking on the success of the trial effort. In education, the best example of feedback is evaluation or testing. The test must be valid and reliable. The input is checked by way of the output and against the criterion for the desired output. All this in education means teaching a specific lesson, applying it, and evaluating to determine whether the lesson was learned. Terminology in education has been long established in the literature as in other professions. Persons unacquainted with the professional literature are likely to try to establish alternatives thus making their efforts rather complex.

Agreements on a standard procedure in systems analysis are hard to come by, yet a simple workable technique is desirable despite the many attending variables. Systems analysis in industry is not as fully established and uniform as is the occupational analysis technique in technical and vocational education.

Diagramming

Organization and flow chart techniques as shown in Figures 4, 5, and 6 are used in whole or in part in spotting doubtful areas of success in the systems analysis approach. Such charts are useful in identifying areas of difficulty when lack of management organization may be suspected, but they are not sufficiently detailed for correcting the weaknesses in the various areas of manpower. A detailed check list of known fundamentals required for successful performance on the job is necessary. Diagramming alone is not detailed enough for training purposes.

Specific Training

Many weaknesses in manufacture and distribution of goods are caused by inadequate training of personnel involved despite the apparent excellence of the management organization. All individuals must be competent in their respective areas of responsibility, including the training personnel. The program of training should be listed in detail and the technique for doing so is not unlike the occupational analysis technique. The term *systems analysis* has been used on occasion in referring to occupational analysis. The need for occupational analysis comes when the area of difficulty has been determined and when training is indicated as remedial. The problem is not solved by identification alone or by merely indicating need for remedial work to overcome the deficiencies. Specific training is needed to complete the series of events that lead to successful solution of the problem that has been identified.

Simplicity is Important

It is unwise and impractical to conceive complex solutions for simple problems. Simplicity is important in all training. There is little justification for attempting to make an impressive show in education by twisting the procedure of occupational analysis for specific areas of training in order to appear impressive. The systems analysis approach is for overall planning—the strategic technique of management.

The higher the echelon of industry and business, the less agreement there seems to be regarding need for a formal correctional procedure to improve production and distribution. Solving the problem of identification alone does not complete the task. The weakness is still there until corrected by one of the several remedial choices including training. The program of training must be in organized form, specific, and not "carried in the head" as one official stated when informed of the need for organized training in a certain area under his direction.

Tradeoff, feedback and alternative actually involve trial and error, which is present in some degree in all learning, but there is less of it when instruction is given in the known fundamentals in the work under consideration as is done in mathematics. How discouraging, and slow, it is for a person who has not had some mathematics instruction to attempt solution of a mathematical problem without a store of mathematical knowledge from which to draw. This is too often referred to as the research approach to teaching. It is absurd to indentify trial and error as research in a learning situation when the learner does not have the apperceptive basis from which to work. Trial and error referred to as research in technical education is often an excuse for evading the effort involved in good teaching, and it is dangerous in areas where machines and materials are involved. It is misuse of the term research.

There must be an apperceptive basis from which to work in order to successfully solve problems in a given area. It is almost futile, and certainly discouraging, and a waste of time, to attempt solution of a problem in any area of world activity and responsibility by means of trial and error, tradeoff for alternatives and often with little success. One may advise on methodology of approach in management without a background of expert technical knowledge and skill in production, but to teach the actual knowhow, to develop such knowledge and skill, requires the apperceptive basis of successful experience in the area under consideration.

Professional Preparation

The making of a check list of fundamental elements of an occupation or phase of it including the skills and related information is the beginning of a series of experiences in education relating to preparation for good teaching. Good teaching doesn't just happen.

The analysis check list may include course material for many hours of training or for only a few depending upon the extent of the occupation. After development of the course there comes the important business of teaching successfully and the attending study of methodology of instructing which is exceedingly important. Then also necessary is ability in evaluation procedures. Related to the success of the foregoing is the study of human relations. The good instructor has the sound judgment-forming ability needed for excellence in teaching which means that he is understanding and tolerant in relation to the learner's efforts.

There is much more than input, tradeoff, feedback and alternatives in the successful teaching of an occupation or phase of it whether in automation or in general production in school or in the world of work outside of school.

Summary

Workers in education should be able to distinguish training analysis from the many techniques of job descriptions, job specifications, the making of organization and flow charts, time and motion study, job classifications and systems analysis. If these are used in attempts to conceive instructional materials, they fail and consequently analysis is assumed to have been of little value. Brief descriptions of a few common forms of analysis have been presented and should be carefully reviewed.

ASSIGNMENTS AND DISCUSSION TOPICS

1. Do you know of analysis techniques other than those mentioned? Discuss them in comparison with any of these listed here.
2. Make a job description for the occupation that you plan to analyze, following the main points of the job description given.
3. Make a job specification, or locate one, for production purposes.
4. How can organization and flow charts be helpful in vocational guidance whether in actual counseling or in direct instruction in the classroom?
5. Discuss the problem of classification of jobs so as to equalize pay according to abilities required to do the work.
6. Does the fact that workers move about, or that machines change, have any relation to the need for training?
7. Would the techniques mentioned here have some value in connection with analysis procedures for training?

FOR FURTHER READING

Allen, C. R., *The Instructor, the Man, and the Job* (Philadelphia: J. B. Lippincott Co., 1919), Chap. 5.

Barnes, R. M., *Motion and Time Study* (New York: John Wiley and Sons, 1958), Chap. 7.

Bowman, C. A., *Graphic Aids in Occupational Analysis* (Milwaukee: The Bruce Publishing Co., 1924).

Christian, R. W., "Work Measurement Today," *Factory*, Vol. 121, No. 9, September, 1963.

Davis, R. C., *Industrial Organization and Management*, 3 ed. (New York: Harper and Brothers, 1957), Chaps. 1, 4, 9, 14, 15, 27.

Dearden, John, and McFarlan, F. Warren, *Management Information Systems* (Homewood, Ill.: Richard D. Irwin, Inc., 1966), Chaps. 1–5.

Eary, D. F., and Johnson, G. E., *Process Engineering for Manufacturing* (Englewood Cliffs, N. J.: Prentice-Hall, Inc., 1962).

Fryklund, Verne C., *Selection and Training of Modern Factory Workers* (Minneapolis: University of Minnesota Press, 1934), Chaps. 1 and 4.

Fryklund, Verne C., "What is Systems Analysis?" *IAVE Magazine*, Vol. 59, No. 4, April, 1970, p. 33.

Koepke, C. A., *Plant Production Control* (New York: John Wiley & Sons, 1961).

Lazzaro, Victor and others, *Systems and Procedures* (Englewood Cliffs, N.J.: Prentice-Hall, Inc., 1959), Chaps. 1–4, 16.

Mayer, R. C., *Production Management* (New York: McGraw-Hill Book Co., 1962), pp. 11–301.

Modne, J. A., "Automation in Scheduling Control," *Automatic Control*, Vol. 18, No. 1, January–February, 1963, pp. 17–19.

Occupational Outlook Handbook. U. S. Department of Labor Statistics, Bulletin Number 1550 (1968–69) Washington, D.C.: United States Government Printing Office.

Optner, L. O., *Systems Analysis for Business and Industrial Problem Solving* (Englewood, N. J.: Prentice-Hall, Inc., 1965).

Piper, Roger. *The Story of Computers.* (New York: Harcourt, Brace and World, Inc., 1964).

Selvidge, R. W., *How to Teach a Trade* (Peoria: C. A. Bennett Co., 1923), Chaps. 1, 2, and 3.

Selvidge, R. W., and Fryklund, V. C., *Principles of Trade and Industrial Teaching* (Peoria: C. A. Bennett Co., 1946), Chaps. 4 and 5.

Warner, W. L., and Abegglen, J. C., *Occupational Mobility in American Business and Industry* (Minneapolis: University of Minnesota Press, 1955).

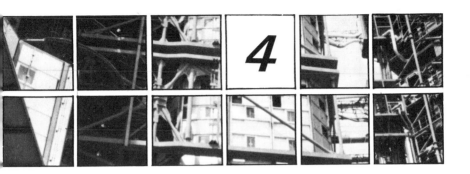

Identifying Occupational Elements — I

To identify elements of an industrial occupation properly, one must know the meaning of certain terms used in designating them. Three important terms, namely, *jobs*, *operations*, and *related information*, should be understood before attempting to make an analysis for instructional purposes. The first two are defined in this chapter, the last is defined in the following chapter.

Two Recognized Meanings

The work that a man does and gets paid for is called his job.[1]

1. Charles R. Allen, *The Instructor, the Man, and the Job* (Philadelphia: J. B. Lippincott Co., 1919), p. 47.

49

Regardless of what he does, whether it is custom work or repetitive work, whether he is a skilled mechanic or an operative, he has a job, a payroll job. The work that he does may require training. Job training means training for an occupation whether the work is simple or complex. The use of the term *job* in connection with what people get paid to do makes it essentially a production term.

Another meaning has been given to it. It is also referred to as a piece of work done, or a completed project; both have about the same meaning.[2] Whether there is reference to a building under construction, a pattern, a casting, a metal vise, a cabinet being made, or a repair assignment, any of these may be referred to as a job. That is, according to this meaning, *job* and *project* are the same. A builder, for example, may refer to the various buildings under construction as job number one, job number two, and so on. Some builders refer to them as projects.

The term *job* is also casually used: "*He does a good job*," "*He is on the job*," "*He botched the job*," and the like. But let us not permit these expressions to confuse the technical meaning of the term *job* in training.

Technically, two meanings have been given the word *job*, therefore. One of these meanings has to do with what one gets paid for, his way of earning a living; the other with what one makes or repairs while learning. There is little difference in the two meanings. In earning a living, one usually gets paid for what he makes whether it is a completed project or part of one. In a vocational-technical school, while preparing for entrance to a skilled technical occupation, a learner may be assigned to the making of a whole project, or he may be assigned to operations on a production basis and rotated to various work stations, but he is not likely to get paid for it. In preparing for entrance to a service occupation, he is likely to be assigned to repair or overhaul a machine. However, under school-training conditions, what he makes or what he repairs is called a job. Under conditions of production training in industry, what he does and gets paid for is also called a job. Training in industry may be on a payroll job even though the worker performs only a single operation or a large number of them. He is trained for a payroll job.

2. R. W. Selvidge, *How to Teach a Trade* (Peoria, Ill.: C. A. Bennett, 1923), Chap. III.

It is not difficult to give samples of payroll jobs in any area of industrial work. One needs only to name what one gets paid for doing. He may be a worker on a drill press, on a shaper, or on a boring mill; he may be a setup man or a toolmaker; he may be an operative or a skilled mechanic, but he gets paid and has a job. If he ceases to be paid, he quits and is out of a job. If a new person is to be trained to take his place, he must be taught the elements of the work under consideration.

The two meanings of the term *job* are briefed below:

PAYROLL JOBS IN PRODUCTION	JOBS IN TRAINING
What the worker gets paid to do.	A completed project or article in a custom occupation.
	OR
His job is a payroll job, but he may perform a number of operations or only one.	A repair or overhaul assignment in a service occupation.
Each operation involves several operating steps—must be taught to a learner.	The learner must master a number of operations in either.
	Each operation involves several operating steps—must be taught to a learner.

The foregoing comparison between the two leads to the elements to be taught. Eventually the elements must be taught either on a payroll job or in school.

The term *job* on the basis of which men are paid was used in production training originally by Allen,[3] and it is an appropriate term because actually men are trained for payroll jobs. Allen refers, however, to the importance of analyzing the jobs into operations for instructional purposes. He refers to instruction on operations.[4]

The term *job* aside from its payroll meaning, and in reference to projects as produced in a custom trade or to repair and overhaul assignments in a service trade, was used first in training by Selvidge.[5] Both meanings of a job can be found in a good dic-

3. Allen, *op. cit.*, p. 47.
4. *Ibid.*, p. 56.
5. Selvidge, *op. cit.*, Chap. III.

tionary. Allen said the job is the instructional unit. Selvidge said the operation is the instructional unit. Both had the same meaning in mind, however, because both believed that the trade or job elements must be taught.

Allen was a scientist and a teacher who did his earlier analysis work in the shipyards for the United States Ship Building Emergency Fleet Corporation during World War I years. Payroll job training was the practice; men were trained for jobs. As has been mentioned, however, he referred to instruction on operations. Selvidge was a mechanical engineer whose work was in the occupational training program of the United States Army. His interest prior to this was in building construction. He was at one time a builder of large structures and later a teacher of engineering shopwork. He held to the "completed whole" concept for the meaning of the term *job* which he took from the dictionary, and said that for teaching purposes the job had to be reduced to its various elements and the elements then had to be taught. Careful study of their writings reveals that their differences were in the use of the term *job* rather than in the fundamental concept of what should be taught.

Not a Consistent Teaching Unit

We see now that jobs may be simple or complex. Some are too complex for single teaching lessons. There are complications, therefore, in the use of this word in referring to an instructional unit. For example, the training of a toolmaker who has a payroll job is quite involved. He cannot be taught his job all at one time. The job in his case cannot be the unit of instruction. It must be broken down into its elements and the elements must be taught one by one, in application, over a period of time. These elements are units of instruction, things to be taught, and they consist of operations and information topics.

The punch-press operative also has a payroll job, and in his case the job can be a unit of instruction because he essentially performs one operation. One must consider the operation rather than the job, therefore, as the unit of instruction whether the payroll job is simple or complex.

Service and Auxiliary Payroll Jobs

The term *job* is not confined to industrial production alone. There are all kinds of payroll jobs. There are jobs that are closely related to production such as making drawings, estimating costs, keeping time, cutting gears, setting up machines, milling lumber, cleaning clothes, and so on. These are service and auxiliary payroll jobs. Anything that one gets paid for, however, is a job. If the job requires considerable instruction for a learner to be successful in it, it must be analyzed into its essential elements before it can effectively be taught.

Many Types of Jobs

Any attempt to classify, according to types, all the different payroll jobs would become involved, and it is unnecessary. *It is important to know that any given kind of work that is worthy and is complicated enough to make instruction necessary should be analyzed into its elements before attempting to teach it*, if *thorough instruction is desired.* However, agreement is necessary on analysis terminology; there must be a common understanding of terms. If there seems to be difficulty in understanding or in agreement, keep in mind that the essential elements or fundamentals of the occupation exist, nevertheless, and they must be identified and taught regardless of what they are called. The terminology used here is the most generally accepted.

DEFINITION OF OPERATION

The operation, as has already been indicated, is a unit of work in a job that involves the making, servicing, or repairing of something.[6] It is best compared to an operation in arithmetic except that it includes materials. Several operations are required in combination in the solution of a problem in arithmetic, and so several operations are required in combination in the making of something in the shop or in the repairing or overhauling of a machine. Whether the term *job* is accepted in training as meaning a completed piece of work, or as something which one gets paid for,

6. Selvidge, *op. cit.*, Chap. IV.

several operations in combination, by hand or machine, may be required to do the job.

Operations Involve Depicting, Forming, Shaping, Assembling

Operations do not assume the mere using of tools and should not be expressed in that way as, for example, "to use compasses" or "to use a knurling tool" or "to use a plane" or "to use a trowel" or "to operate a torch." Operations are more than that; they are definite things to do; they are units of work that involve the depicting, or forming, or shaping of materials, or the assembling of parts.[7] One or several tools may be used in performing a particular operation. It is meaningless, therefore, to attempt to identify an operation in terms of the "use of a tool" or "the operation of a machine." To be more exact, the expression "to use compasses" should be put in terms of depicting as, for example, "to draw arcs and circles." Other *depicting operations* are "to make a layout," "to lay out centers," "to make an end view," or "to ink arcs and circles." Each of these operations involves more than one tool. Each stands by itself and has some unity but it would be rather valueless alone. Each is combined with other operations in creating something. A *depicting operation*, therefore, has to do with sketching, laying out, or drafting something.

If an operation were identified as the "use of a tool," as, for example, "to use a plane," it would mean that several different ways of using the tool and several practical applications would have to be taught in one lesson. This would be difficult because there frequently are many uses for a given tool, and it may be used in different ways in different operations, and several tools may be used in a given operation. When teaching an operation, however, one teaches the use of the several tools involved, whether hand tools or machine tools, as they appear in their particular applied situations. The nature of the work to be done determines how the tools should be used. By identifying the operation in terms of something to be shaped, or formed, or assembled, or depicted, its meaning is clear and it defines exactly what is to be taught.

A *forming operation* refers to the changing of material by heat-

7. Allen, *op. cit.*, p. 49.

ing or welding or molding or bending, and so on. Examples are "to upset," "to ram the drag," "to bend eyes over the horn," "to make a parting," or "to make a bead weld." It would be less meaningful if, in the above order, these forming operations were expressed in terms of the uses of tools such as "to use a forge hammer," "to use a ram," "to use a hammer and a horn," "to use parting sand," or "to operate a welding torch."

A *shaping operation* has to do with changing the shape of materials with edge tools or by grinding as, for example, "to plane an edge," "to tap a hole," "to drawfile," or "to hand ream." It is not difficult to see how indefinite it would be if these operations were expressed thus, "to use a plane," "to use a tap," "to use a file," or "to use a reamer."

Assembling operations involve the assembling of parts. Assembling operations in certain occupations frequently follow a series of operations that include depicting, forming, and shaping. With few exceptions, assembling follows other operations such as in printing, where ready formed type is assembled, and in service occupations such as auto mechanics, where sections are disassembled and assembled for overhaul. Assembling operations are common in service occupations. Examples of assembling operations in custom work are "place a feeder head," "assemble cope on the drag of pattern," "set a line of type," or "fit brushes to the motor."

Occasionally an operation may seem to involve considerable knowledge, thus raising doubt whether it should be called an operation or an information topic. If it includes some measure of manipulative or machine work, it should be called an operation.

Inspection and Testing

Inspecting and testing operations sometimes are overemphasized in importance in identifying essential elements of a trade. In production in industry, inspection and testing have important places, but in instruction they have limitations as units of instruction. Inspection and testing are continuously integrated in all instructional work; they accompany all learning efforts in technical work. There is no particular reason for attempting to create inspectional and testing operations in analysis because they usually form part of, or steps in, an operation.

Some payroll job workers are called inspectors in industry, but their duties are often related to existing operations, and usually the training required is limited to the ability to perform the operation being inspected, or to recognize it, or to inspect a part to see that it has been made according to certain standards. Many of these inspectors are not mechanics at all. They have been trained merely to do certain inspectional work that involves judgment and the application of certain standards of measurement or quality to a given product or piece of work.

There is little reason for identifying "inspectional operations" in mechanical occupations. Inspection and testing usually involve steps in an operation performed by the mechanic to see that work is proceeding properly. For example, "test the truth of alignment with a test indicator" is a step in the operation "to align a tail-stock center" and certain other machine-shop operations. There are exceptional instances when inspectional and testing operations appear, but they are more the exception than the rule. There are not enough of them at least to consider inspection and testing among the words that characterize operations.

Expressing an Operation

It is good teaching to state definitely what is to be done. The learner has a right to know what he is expected to learn, and it is not made clear when the *use* of tools and *operation* of machines appear in attempts to identify operations. Avoid them and you lessen the temptation to take the easy and less meaningful way. The actual performance, the thing to be done, the depicting or shaping or forming or assembling procedure should be indicated.

An operation should be expressed in the future tense as an order to do something specific. It is to occur in the future and is not taking place now. Therefore, the infinitive form *to* rather than the present participle form *ing* should be used. As, for example, "to knurl in the lathe" would be better form than "knurling in the lathe." This is not serious, but the former is a specific, definite statement, an order to do something. The latter has a suggestion of generality about it and assumes something already taking place.

The participle form is used in titles of books, but an operation in analysis is not a title. It is a direction to do something specific. It might be suggested that the adverb *how* be attached so as to read "how to knurl in the lathe." However, when all operations are expressed thus, there is monotony or a sameness about it. The infinitive form "to knurl in the lathe" assumes *how* placed before it. To leave off *how to* and assume its presence would be even better and it is recommended as, for example, "knurl in the lathe." Each statement thus would not have a mechanical sameness about it.

Related information topics presented in Chapter 5 have latitude and usually are not as definite and limited in scope as are operations. Therefore, the *ing* form is used in designating them as, for example, "making steel" rather than "how to make steel." An information topic must have a title and the participle form for the title is proper. This topic does not assume a marked and definite coverage as does "how to knurl." There can be limitation or expansion as necessary in an information topic. An operation is something specific to do.

If you use the *directive* form in the statement of an operation, and the *title* form for an information topic, you can readily and quickly identify them when necessary.

An operation should also be expressed without reference to a particular job in the trade. That is, an operation is usable on any job that requires the particular operation, along with others. Therefore the statement of the operation should be such as to make it applicable on any job requiring it, as, for example, "to knurl" and not "to knurl micrometer handles." The lesson on knurling should be applicable wherever knurling is necessary, and it should be stated so it will not be assumed for application on one job only. There should be many jobs to choose from in teaching how to knurl and not just one available in each shop.

If an operation sheet or a visual aid is desired, it should be prepared so it can be used on any job that includes that operation. This saves the making of a new sheet or aid for teaching a particular operation for every new application of it. Once an operation sheet or visual aid has been prepared, it should be usable on many jobs. The title of it, or the statement of the operation, should be in keeping with the idea of flexibility of application.

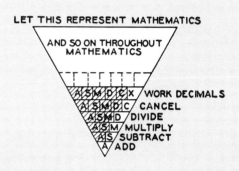

Fig. 7. *The accumulative nature of operations in arithmetic. Starting with* a, *one first learns to add. One must add in order to subtract. When teaching subtraction, the new element in subtraction,* s, *is built on the old addition,* a, *shown in the shaded portion. One must be able to add* a, *and subtract* s, *in order to multiply. Elements* a, s, *and* m *compose multiplication, but when teaching how to multiply, only* m *needs to be taught. In order to cancel, one must first know how to do* a, s, m, *and* d. *Only the new element* c *needs to be taught, though the operation* how to cancel *is composed of* a, s, m, d, *and* c. *And so the operations throughout mathematics accumulate, but each operation has identity of its own.*

Auxiliary Operations

Many operations are of an auxiliary nature. That is, they are not directly involved in producing something, but they are necessary to keep production going. For instance, it is necessary to sharpen tools, to grind bits, to clean equipment, to adjust or to change devices and attachments, and so on. Instructions are necessary for such operations and, therefore, they should be included in the analysis of the work. They are auxiliary operations. They need not be listed separately nor labeled as auxiliary operations. It is important, however, to know that they are operations rather than jobs.

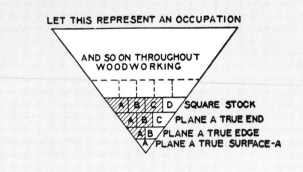

Fig. 8. *The accumulative nature of operations in woodworking. One starts with learning to plane a true surface* a. *One must be able* to plane a true surface *in order* to plane a true edge. *When teaching* how to plane a true edge, *the new element* b *is added to the old element* a, *shown in the shaded portion. One must be able to do* a *and* b *in order to* plane a true end. *Elements* a, b, *and* c *compose the planing of a true end, but when teaching it, only* c *needs to be taught. In order* to square stock, *one must be able to do* a, b, c, *and* d. *Only the new element* d *needs to be taught, though the operation* how to square stock *is composed of* a, b, c, *and* d. *And so the operations throughout woodworking accumulate, but each operation has identity of its own.*

Cumulative Nature of Operations

Operations are cumulative in nature as are the operations in mathematics. Cancellation, for example, is an essential element in mathematics that involves elementary operations such as addition, division, and multiplication, plus the principle of canceling, as is shown graphically in Figure 7. Cancellation in turn becomes part of more advanced mathematical operations. And as one continues into the advanced phases of mathematics, the more cumulative in nature the operations become.

Most operations in a mechanical occupation are of a cumulative nature. In woodworking, "to plane a true surface" is an operation that appears again in another more advanced operation "to square stock" (see Figure 8). The latter appears in many other operations as in "to make a table top," and so on. In drafting also, elementary operations appear as part of more advanced operations. In machine shop, laying-out operations appear again as part of many advanced operations. And so in the beginning of an occupation, there are elementary units that appear again as part of more advanced ones. Without training in the more elementary units, the learner would be seriously handicapped as he attempts the more advanced work. Understanding of this principle simplifies the problem for the individual who is attempting to make an analysis of an occupation for teaching purposes. The technique for identifying the more elementary and frequently used units is presented in Chapter 6.

Occupational Elements Are Constant

Just as the essential elements in mathematics are thought of as constant, so also are the essential elements of an occupation. The elements of mathematics that Leonardo Da Vinci used in solving the problems of his day are the same elements that are used in solving mathematical problems today. But the problems have changed. Leonardo was not faced with the solution of problems such as confront the mathematician of today. New mathematical problems are connected with the designing of our many modern machines, and the machines are continually changing, but the elements of mathematics remain quite the same.

Compare the washing machine of twenty years ago with the washing machine of today. It has changed much in appearance, but practically all the patternmaking, foundry, and machine-shop operations needed in making the machine of today are the same as those used in making the machine of twenty years ago. The essential elements are rather constant. They are constant with the history of the occupation, but the projects or jobs are changing. Changing technology affects the projects more than it does the essential operations involved in making the projects. There are improved tools and machines to do the work more readily, but the operations are quite the same. Operations are constant also with respect to geographical locations. For example, machine-shop operations in an eastern city would be the same in a midwestern or a western city. And the machine-shop operations performed in an adding-machine factory would be the same in principle as those performed in an agricultural-machine factory. Machine-shop operations in this country have counterparts in other countries.

Technological development has brought new materials, but essential elements of performance for forming or shaping the materials remain quite standard, although the articles change rapidly in design and in use. Technological development also has led to an increase in the number of service occupations.

Eight Important Points in Identifying Operations

There are eight important points that stand out in determining what an operation is. They are criteria for identifying operations.

1. It occurs frequently in an occupation with considerable uniformity of content; it is relatively constant in time and geographically.
2. It involves teachable content.
3. It is a distinct unit which, when completed, makes the worker feel that he has come to a good stopping place.
4. It has its greatest value when combined with other operations; alone it is usually of little value.
5. The length is such as to make suitable content for a class demonstration.
6. When it is put with other operations in combination, they produce or service something larger without gaps or overlapping between them.
7. It involves depicting, shaping, forming, or assembling.
8. It can be broken down into definite steps of procedure.

Operations as Skills

Operations are occasionally called skills. There is no particular reason for this, nor is it undesirable. It is a casual expression often used in referring to manual dexterity. Dictionary definitions do not limit the meaning of skill to manual performance; they include mental abilities as well. Many kinds of skills are involved in mental work and in manual work.

Operations and Payroll Jobs

It is seldom that an operation becomes a completed whole, a project or a job in the instructional meaning of the term. However, it may become a job at any time from the point of view of the payroll. One may have a job drilling holes but he would still be performing an operation. If a woodworker were making a drawer and fitting it to a table that he was constructing, he would be performing a cumulative operation. But if he were a specialist in a furniture factory and made only table drawers he would have a payroll job, and what he made could be referred to by the observer as a job. He would nevertheless be performing an operation.

The word *job* is not a good term to use in identifying essential elements to be taught. It seems awkward to refer to the following as jobs: "to draw arcs and circles," "to draw horizontal lines," "to set leaders," "to cut insulation," and "to cut a gate." If the term *job* means payroll job or something one gets paid for, it is difficult to find payroll jobs limited to these performances. They are small units, essential elements, that form part of something larger. They are operations according to definition.

Other definitions have been given the term *operation*, and it would be well for the student to look them up in a large dictionary. Only one of the definitions refers readily to instruction, however.

The term *job*, when used to identify instructional units, is sometimes justified because it is assumed to be an industrial practice, since it is a term from industry. Industry, however, does not often refer to the assignments of repetitive workers as jobs. They are payroll jobs, but the men perform operations and the men in repetitive work are called operatives or operators. When the men are instructed on the job by foremen, they are taught how to perform the operations. There are many good reasons, therefore, for referring to the manipulative essential elements as operations.

Operations and Processes

Operations are frequently called processes. There is interchangeability of use between the two terms. Process is also defined as a series of operations in the production of something. This term is often used technically in relation to chemical action. Inasmuch as operations are cumulative in nature, it is difficult to distinguish the two terms *operations* and *processes*. There seems to be no point or line of separation that sets off operations from processes. The expression "operations and processes" has no particular value other than to mean operations or processes. The use of these two terms together is clearly repetitious.

Job Operations

It has been difficult for many persons to distinguish jobs from operations both as to the payroll meaning and the instructional meaning of the terms. In several published papers the expression "job operation" has been used in referring to the manipulative essential elements or operations. There seems to be no reason for it except to make certain that the unit is practical and can be applied. If it is an operation, it is practical and has both instructional value and payroll meaning. In combining the two words, nothing in particular is gained. If in doubt as to whether to call a given unit a *job* or *operation*, it would be satisfactory to call it an *instructional unit* which it surely is if it is an element to be taught.

Summary

Two meanings have been given the term *job:* one has to do with what one gets paid for, his payroll job; the other with what one makes. In training, whether on a payroll job or in school, the elements of the job must be taught.

The job does not make a consistent teaching unit because some payroll jobs are simple and some are complex. The work of a drill-press operative may be simple enough to make it possible to assume the job as an instructional unit. Yet the operation is also the instructional unit because the drill-press operative performs an operation repetitively and gets paid for it. However, the payroll job of tool and diemaker presents a problem if the job is assumed to be the instructional unit. It is too complex. The elements must be identified and taught. They are the operations and information topics. Whatever the interpretation of the word *job*, the elements must be taught if training is intended.

Many kinds of payroll jobs are not directly connected with production. Some are service and some are auxiliary jobs. It is not important to classify them. The important thing to know is that if training is involved, and if the job requires considerable ability, analysis is necessary to determine what should be taught.

The operation is a unit of work that can be compared to an operation in arithmetic. Just as it takes several operations in combination to solve a problem in arithmetic, so it takes several operations in combination to produce or repair something. Operations do not concern the mere using of tools. They are units of work that involve depicting, forming, shaping, or assembling. The various uses of tools are covered step by step in the operations. There may be several tools in a given operation and the use of each is taught as it comes into service.

It is a good idea not to allow the word *use* to appear in indicating an operation. The actual performance, the thing to be done, should be listed. It is confusing to call "use a jack plane" an operation. It would be clearer to say "plane a surface true and smooth," or "plane an edge," or "plane an end," or "plane a chamfer." Operations have specific meaning, whereas "use a jack plane" may mean any one or all of the many ways to use a plane. And so with other tools. Furthermore, if one wishes to be even more specific in indicating an operation, the infinitive form *how to* is better than the participle form *ing*; for example, "how to knurl in the lathe" is better than "knurling in the lathe." The former is specific and it is to be done in the future. The *ing* form serves best in titles as in information topics, and it is in the present tense.

There are operations of auxiliary nature that are not directly involved in production. It is necessary to condition tools and equipment or to cut materials in order to keep production going. An example of such an operation is "dress a screwdriver" or "sharpen a cold chisel." It is not necessary to list them separately, but they should be included in the analysis.

Eight important characteristics listed in the chapter are helpful in identifying operations. Operations are sometimes called *skills*, *processes*, and *job operations*. Whatever they are called the elements of operations must be taught. The elements are constant with the history of the occupation and with respect to geographical locations and types of factories. The elements can always properly be called instructional units if there seems doubt as to whether one of several designations is appropriate.

ASSIGNMENTS AND DISCUSSION TOPICS

1. Make up a list of five simple payroll jobs that you believe would require but a few weeks' training for successful work in any of them.
2. Make up a list of five rather complex industrial payroll jobs that you believe would require a year or more of training to qualify a worker in any one of them.
3. List a dozen or more operations from your occupation. Do not include the word *use* in listing them.
4. List several auxiliary operations in your occupation.
5. List several advanced operations that include elementary ones plus a new principle which together make a new operation to teach.
6. Describe a situation in which a payroll job consists mainly of performing a single operation. Describe a situation in which a payroll job involves many operations.
7. Do you believe that unskilled or low-skilled operations need to be listed in making an analysis? Why?
8. Tell all you can about an operation, its meaning, how to express it, points of recognition, and so on.

FOR FURTHER READING

Allen, C. R., *The Instructor, the Man, and the Job* (Philadelphia: J. B. Lippincott Co., 1919), Chap. 7.

Cushman, Frank, *Training Procedure* (New York: John Wiley and Sons, 1940), Chap. 3.

Fryklund, Verne C., *Trade and Job Analysis* (Milwaukee: The Bruce Publishing Company, 1947).

Giachino, J. W., and Gallington, R. O., *Course Construction in Industrial Arts and Vocational Education* (Chicago: American Technical Society, 1961).

Jackey, D. F., and Barlow, L. B., *The Craftsman Prepares to Teach* (New York: The Macmillan Company, 1944).

Rose, Homer C., *Development and Supervision of Training Programs* (Chicago: American Technical Society, 1964).

Selvidge, R. W., *How to Teach a Trade* (Peoria: C. A. Bennett Company, 1923), Chaps. 3 and 4.

Selvidge, R. W., and Fryklund, V. C., *Principles of Trade and Industrial Teaching* (Peoria: C. A. Bennett Co., 1946), Chaps. 4 and 5.

Silvius, G. H., and Bohn, R. C., *Organizing Course Materials* (Bloomington, Ill.: McKnight and McKnight Publishing Co., 1961).

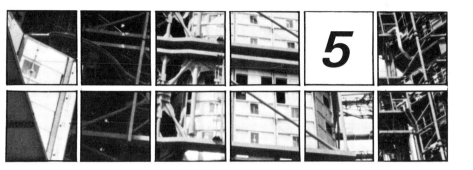

Identifying Occupational Elements — II

RELATED INFORMATION

Related Information and Related Subjects

Related information is the information that the workman should have and which should be taught by the teacher to a learner of a given occupation. It should not be confused with the term *related subjects* as used in designating certain reimbursable academic offerings in the federally aided program of vocational education. The related subjects may be taught by other than the shop teachers, and often in rooms separated from the shop. For example, in technical teacher training, when the analysis of an occupation is made, it usually covers the work of one teacher for one occupation, or phase of it, and is limited to what is taught in one laboratory or shop under one instructor.

The technique of occupational analysis can be applied in analyzing the related subjects. For example, there could be a complete analysis of mathematics for machinists and it would be helpful to the teacher of related mathematics for machinists. It would be extensive, and would require the cooperation of the related mathematics and the machine-shop teachers. But the machine-shop teacher in making his analysis would include only the mathematics that he must teach in his shop to meet immediate needs. He would teach the related information and not the related subject. The learner and the shop teacher would be handicapped if they had to wait for the related-subjects instructor to teach a few simple principles of mathematics involved in the use of the micrometer. It would be necessary for the shop teacher to teach the units at the time of need, but at some time the related mathematics instructor would go into considerable detail in teaching mathematics principles and mathematics of the machinist together; and he would need a rather detailed analysis of it.

System, Yet Simplicity

System and organization are indeed necessary in this day of rapid technical progress, but when a system for teaching becomes so involved that it keeps a person busy making it work, then there is need for less system and more simplicity. We must not attempt to make our materials look formidable for the benefit of outsiders, and at the same time deprive ourselves of their use because they are too complex. Simplicity, therefore, should be a guiding word in analyzing any occupation for teaching purposes.

Sound psychology and good logic should be exercised when attempting to organize instructional material for teaching purposes. There should be a plan that follows the things to be taught as they actually appear in practical working situations. A new teacher should not be required to undertake an analysis of an occupation just to make it; nor should the analysis be so complex that it confuses him when he tries to use it. Unnecessary classification and reclassification of related information is one of the overdone phases of analysis that should be carefully studied with a view to simplification.

It is exceedingly difficult even for experienced teachers to follow from one occupation to another the meanings of many terms, such as auxiliary information, job knowledge, trade knowledge, related knowledge, related trade content, trade technical knowledge, marginal information, job information, and so on. There is little uniformity in identification and interpretation of meanings of these classifications by the untrained. Attempts to make distinctions and applications have resulted in unnecessarily detailed analyses. Analysis must be practical. It must be simple and useful.

Fine Classifications Unnecessary

The breaking-up of information topics into fine classifications and the listing of the separate classifications under separate subject headings, as shown in Figure 16, page 119, is difficult and unnecessary. In order to teach such information, the parts must be put together again by the teacher. Such an analysis places a burden on the teacher. It hinders rather than helps him. It merely makes the instructional material look impressive to the person who does not know otherwise, but it is of little help to the teacher who is supposed to use it. Moreover, unnecessary informational detail frequently results in disagreement and confusion in identification of assignments for related-subjects teachers, coordinators, and shop teachers.

The fundamentals of a technical occupation include related information topics as well as the work. The workman must have this information and be able to use some of it in forming judgments in doing his work, and some of it should be helpful to him in other ways. Related information topics, however, should not be confused with certain detailed points of knowledge that are integral parts of the operations.[1] There are items of auxiliary knowledge that are part of every operation, and must be included when teaching the operation. They are taught on the work or on the "spot" as part of a demonstration. It is quite impossible to perform an operation without certain thought processes and points of knowledge—"headwork"—that help make the unit and give it existence. These items of knowledge involve the *how* and the *why* and safe methods, and so on.

1. C. R. Allen, *The Instructor, the Man and the Job* (Philadelphia: J. B. Lippincott Co., 1919), pp. 54–62, and Chap. XIII.

These items of knowledge and performance, which in combination make the operation, should not be separated from each other when making the analysis. They form a pattern and there is little reason for separating them on paper when they must be put together again when teaching. The reason for teaching an operation is to *tell how* and *show how* it is done.

The real related information topics are major units which, like operations, have entity of their own and hold rank in importance with them, but they are not parts of the operations. They are of such nature as to be independent lessons in themselves.

Three Kinds of Information

In learning an occupation which is complicated enough to be made up of fundamental elements, three kinds of information topics are involved. These topics are listed separately in an analysis of an occupation and one, the first, has a priority in the teaching order.

1. One kind has to do with *information that the worker must know* in order to form judgments in doing his work. Without this information he would be handicapped, and in some industrial occupations he could not be classified as more than a helper. For example, it takes more than manipulative ability to qualify as a skilled mechanic. Certain information is required. Some facts are directly related and some are indirectly related to the whole job, but the worker must know both. *Such information should be listed separately and taught in advance of other topics.* Included are informational details which involve mathematics, science, technical terms, safety, art in some trades, English, economics, or psychology in others.[2] Many other subjects may be represented, depending on the nature of the occupation. If the information *must be known* in order to form judgments, the subjects represented usually are of technical nature. Any information topics in this group are classified for convenience under the heading of *technical information*. This is a term that applies to any kind of information that will help the worker in forming judgments whether the information is direct or indirect in its use. A few samples of technical information follow. They are topics only and should be outlined when making the complete analysis.

2. Allen, *op. cit.*, pp. 48 and 170–173.

MACHINE SHOP

1. Reading Working Drawings
2. Cutting Speeds and Feeds
3. Calculations for Tapers
4. Indexing Calculators
5. Abrasives and Coolants

MECHANICAL DRAFTING

1. Clearances, Finishes, Tolerances, Fillets
2. Machine-Shop Operations
3. Instruments and Their Care
4. Dimensioning Rules
5. Threads, Bolts, Screws

SHEET METALWORKING

1. Sheet Metals and Their Uses
2. Solders and Fluxes
3. Areas, Volumes, Circumferences
4. Soldering Coppers
5. General Safety Rules

PRINTING

1. Printer's Measurements
2. Printing Papers
3. Rules for Composition
4. Classification of Type Faces
5. Principles of Display

UNBLEACHED SULPHITE PULP MANUFACTURE

1. Sulphite Cooking Acid
2. Wood-Chip Cooking
3. Pulp Treatment
4. Gaskets
5. Valves

DRUGSTORE SELLING

1. Pure-Food Laws
2. Licenses
3. Child-Labor Regulations
4. Customer Buying Motives
5. Safety Precautions

RADIO SERVICE

1. Radio Symbols and Schematics
2. Common Oscillator Troubles
3. A.C. Power Supply
4. Loop Antenna Troubles
5. Auto-Radio Power Supply Circuit

ELECTRIC ARC WELDING

1. Electricity of Welding
2. Types of Electrodes
3. Nomenclature of Joints
4. Welding Symbols
5. Heat and Mechanical Treatment of Welds

PHOTOGRAPHY

1. Camera Classification
2. Filters and Filter Factors
3. Composition in Photography
4. Aperture and Shutter Speeds
5. Light-Meter Technique

INDUSTRIAL ELECTRONICS

1. Theory of Electro-magnetism
2. Power Calculation
3. Theory of Eddy Currents
4. Control of Electric Generators
5. Saturable Core Reactors

PHYSICAL TESTING LABORATORY

1. Principles of X-ray Generator
2. Characteristics of Beta and Gamma Rays
3. Design of Radiation Detection Equipment
4. Viscosity and Surface Tension in Liquid Penetrants
5. Design of Magnetic-Particle Testing

1. Ghosts and Causes
2. Characteristics of a Good Oscilloscope
3. Types of Video I.F. Systems
4. Differentiating Circuits
5. Rectifier-Tube Characteristics

PRIVATE FLIGHT TRAINING

1. Engine Maintenance Regulations
2. Student-Pilot Limitations
3. CAA Private-Pilot Regulations
4. CAA Commercial-Pilot Regulations
5. Judging Wind Velocities

CLOTHING

1. Choice of Seam Finishes in Relation to Fabrics
2. Availability of Patterns
3. Criteria for a Well-Fitted Garment
4. Selection of Sewing Equipment
5. Common Machine Troubles

TOOL DESIGN

1. Calculate Circular Form Tool Dimensions
2. Tool-Design Principles
3. Heat Treatment of Metals
4. Cutting Speeds and Feeds
5. Standard Parts

ADVANCED ELECTRONICS

1. Systems of Units
2. Atoms and Electrons
3. Basic Electrical Units
4. R-L-C Circuits
5. Resonance

Workmen must know all of these topics in the occupations represented or they will be seriously handicapped in forming the judgments necessary to do their work properly. These are classified as technical information topics regardless of the subject area to which they may seem to belong.

2. There is a *second kind of related information* that should be considered in making an analysis of an occupation: *information which is desirable and good for the mechanic to know but which is not necessary to do the work properly.* The worker can really do his work without it because it is not of judgment-forming value in production or in repair work. It is more general than specific in value. It is concerned with social, economic, and indirect scientific aspects of the occupation. While it is information that the mechanic could do without, yet if he knew it, he would be more enlightened concerning his work and its world relationships, its value and importance to society. Whereas technical information is thought of as a *must*, this second kind of information is *nice to know*. Inasmuch as it is of general nature, it is called *general*

information.[3] It is frequently referred to as socioeconomic information, but this limits the meaning when there also are topics involving science and other subjects in the group. They are classified as general information topics regardless of the subject area to which they may seem to belong. There frequently are topics relating to science that are not necessary to know but which have broadening values, just as do the socioeconomic topics. It is appropriate therefore to identify this *nice-to-know* information of general nature by calling it *general information.* It is an easy term to remember. Many subject areas are represented in an analysis. To identify each topic according to the subject area is unnecessary and cumbersome.

When training time is limited, this sort of information should be left out. This would hold true in war training or in war-production training.

An example of general information of a scientific nature would be a topic that describes the method of making paper. It would be good for the printer to know how paper is made, but it would not be necessary for him to know it in order to do his work properly. A few examples of general-information topics appear below. They are taken from the same occupations that were used in sampling the technical-information topics. Each topic would be outlined in making the complete analysis.

MACHINE SHOP

1. History of Drilling
2. Manufacture of Iron and Steel
3. Shapers in the Tool and Die Industry
4. Development of the Lathe
5. Making of Grinding Wheels

PRINTING

1. Printing in America
2. Invention of Printing
3. Gutenberg, Caxton, Caslon, Bodoni, Goudy, Manutius
4. Papermaking
5. Composition of Books

3. Allen, *op. cit.,* p. 104.

MECHANICAL DRAFTING
1. Metals in Manufacture
2. Engineering and Art
3. Development of Reproduction Devices
4. Drafting Papers and Manufacture
5. World Language

SHEET METALWORKING
1. Manufacture of Sheet Iron
2. Manufacture of Galvanized Iron
3. Manufacture of Copper
4. Manufacture of Tin Plate
5. Socioeconomic Importance of Tin

DRUGSTORE SELLING
1. The Early Drugstore
2. Manufacture of Light Paper Articles
3. Development of Patent Medicine
4. Ready Prescriptions
5. Changing Trends in Drugstore Merchandising

INDUSTRIAL ELECTRONICS
1. Areas of Service
2. Manufacture of Wire
3. New Electrical Products
4. History of Electricity
5. History of Magnetism

RADIO SERVICE
1. Radio Publications
2. Radio Merchandising
3. Government Aids to Radiomen
4. History of Radio
5. Manufacturer's Service

ELECTRIC ARC WELDING
1. Manufacture of Ferrous Metals
2. Metalworking Processes
3. History of Arc Welding
4. Physical Metallurgy
5. Copper and Its Alloys

UNBLEACHED SULPHITE PULP MANUFACTURE
1. History of the Sulphite Process of Pulp
2. Manufacture of Paper and Paperboard
3. Use of Sulphite Waste Liquor
4. Manufacture of Other Kinds
5. Pulp Bleaching

PHOTOGRAPHY
1. History of Photography
2. Manufacture of Printing Papers
3. Manufacture of Film
4. Buying a Camera
5. Sending Pictures by Wire

TELEVISION SERVICE
1. History of Television
2. Manufacture of Picture Tubes
3. Manufacture of Power Transformers
4. Pay vs. Free Television
5. Educational Channels

PRIVATE FLIGHT TRAINING
1. Atmosphere and Its Composition
2. History of Flight
3. Mercator Chart
4. Earth a Rotating Sphere
5. Aircraft Production Industry

CLOTHING	TOOL DESIGN
1. History of Sewing Machines	1. Mining
2. Development of Paper Patterns	2. Production Methods
	3. History of Machine Tools
3. Development of Synthetic Fibers	4. Plant Organization
	5. Hydraulics
4. Clothing Production in the Colonies	
5. Influence of Fibers on Fashion	

Occasionally there may be informational topics that are difficult to identify as either technical or general. If there is doubt and if there is information that seemingly is of judgment-forming value along with information of general nature in a given topic, such a topic should be considered as technical so as not to leave out, in teaching, any of the phases of it that are necessary to know.

3. *There is a third kind of related information, the kind that has vocational guidance value.* Vocational guidance is an all-school function and it involves information related to choosing, preparing for, securing, holding, and making progress in an occupation. Information topics that are helpful in counseling learners in relation to these points should be included in the analysis of an occupation. Vocational guidance in vocational education was thought unnecessary at one time inasmuch as the learners were assumed to have made their choices. This may be true in many cases, but instruction is necessary also on how to obtain a job and how to hold it after one gets it. Then, too, one may desire to make progress in his vocation, and instruction is necessary on the various ways of doing it. There should be instruction covering such topics as employer-employee relations. Not only is there a problem of choosing and preparing for a job but there is much attendant learning involved in making good on the job. Vocational guidance embraces all of these. Inasmuch as technical education sends young people into more jobs than does any other single school service, vocational guidance should be included in the technical program. Emphasis should be given to guidance in industrial arts.

Topics of importance in connection with all aspects of guidance should therefore be included in an analysis of an occupation. Places should be found for these topics in all peacetime technical instruction. Of course, in emergency training this sort of information would be unnecessary.

Examples of guidance topics that accompany the occupations already sampled are presented.

MACHINE SHOP
1. Occupational Opportunities for Machinists
2. The Successful Machinist
3. Opportunities for Advancement
4. Jobbing Shop Ownership
5. Employer-Employee Relations

RADIO SERVICE
1. Careers in Radio Service
2. Training and Educational Opportunities
3. Radio Engineering
4. Radio Operating
5. Radio Servicing as a Business

MECHANICAL DRAFTING
1. Opportunities in the Drafting Trade
2. Work of the Mechanical Engineer
3. Opportunities for Advancement
4. Training for Draftsmen
5. Other Kinds of Drafting

SHEET METALWORKING
1. Increasing Use of Sheet Metal and Its Socioeconomic Implications
2. Opportunities in the Small Shop and in Industry
3. Sheet Metal in Modern Design
4. Employer-Employee Relations
5. Training for the Sheet Metal-Worker

PRINTING
1. Printing Trade
2. Opportunities in Printing
3. Ethics in Trade
4. Hints for Young Printers
5. Apprenticeship, High School, Trade School, College

UNBLEACHED SULPHITE PULP MANUFACTURE
1. Trends in the Pulp Industry
2. The Sulphite Process in the Pulp Industry
3. Opportunities in the Pulp Industry
4. Labor Laws
5. Employer-Employee Relations

DRUGSTORE SELLING
1. Opportunities in the Drugstore Business
2. Owning a Drugstore
3. The Pharmacist
4. Ethics of the Drug Business
5. Departmental Growth

INDUSTRIAL ELECTRONICS
1. Cooperative Training Programs
2. Opportunities in Industrial Electronics
3. State Industrial Commission
4. Apprenticeship and Training Standards
5. Advancement and Education

Other Classifications Unnecessary

All related information that would be included in the analysis of an occupation can therefore be classified under these headings— *technical, general, and guidance.* These are simple classifications which will include any sort of information related to any occupation under consideration. Other detailed designations or classifications are unnecessary. It is not difficult to judge whether certain information topics *must be known* by the worker. It is not a question of whether such information is called mathematics, science, art, or the like. The question is whether it is necessary to know rather than whether it has an academic subject-designation attached. Moreover, it is not necessary to separate the topics into subject groups. Any necessary-to-know information for a particular occupation should be placed in the technical-information classification. It is not difficult to judge whether certain information topics are only nice to know and whether, therefore, they should be placed under the less important group of topics called general information. It is also easy to identify the guidance topics. Experience has shown that shop teachers, related-subjects teachers, and coordinators find that their work assignments are readily classified when these three simple classifications are used.

It is unwise and confusing to establish more categories of information than the three aforementioned ones. For example, socioeconomic information, safety information, trade information, and so on need not be identified separately. The information is either necessary or just nice to know. Some beginning technical teachers have difficulty in determining whether a certain information unit is socioeconomic or something else, and it makes little difference whether it is. They do need to know whether they *must* teach it or *may* teach it if it is nice to know.

Doubtful Interpretations of Related Information

It has been stated that topics of related information *should not be identified* as the "headwork" or auxiliary knowledge that gives meaning to the operations. Let us consider this further because in the analysis procedure the operations are broken down into steps or points as presented in Chapter 7. These steps make certain that every part of an operation is fully covered when demonstrated, and if an operation sheet is to be written or technical writing is undertaken, it serves as an outline. These steps should be listed in their proper sequence so they will follow exactly the actual performance. Some steps are of manual or *doing* nature and some are of informational or *knowing* nature, and some steps combine varying degrees of both *doing* and *knowing*. In the learning and habit-forming processes, these knowing and doing steps combine to give meaning to the operation.

To illustrate this point more fully examples of machine-shop operations broken down into steps are presented.

LATHE OPERATION
How to File Cylindrical Work

OPERATING STEPS:
1. Select mill file.

2. Double speed used for turning.
3. Very little filing needed. Too much filing will cause uneven, inaccurate work.
4. File with long, slow strokes, little pressure.
   Caution: File left-handed to avoid striking dog.
5. Release pressure on return stroke, prevents wire edge on serrations.
6. Overlap with each succeeding stroke of file.
7. File to smooth surface.

SHAPER OPERATION
How to Finish Cut Horizontally

OPERATING STEPS:
1. Grind, set finishing tool.
2. Set fine feed, very coarse if for flat tool finish.
3. If same tool is used for roughing and finishing, it is necessary only to keep it sharp; change feed.
4. Turn on power.
5. Engage clutch.
6. Hand feed to finish size.
7. Engage feed mechanism.

Note that steps 3, 4, 5, 6, 7 (lathe) and steps 1, 4, 5, 6, 7 (shaper) are mostly manipulative, and steps 1, 2 (lathe) and steps 2, 3 (shaper) are mostly informational. There are items of auxiliary knowledge that must be taught on the "spot." Note also that it is difficult to classify all of these steps as wholly manipulative or wholly informational. There may be fusion of knowing and doing even within the steps. It is a question of degree of each. Perhaps there is more emphasis on doing in the illustrative shaper-operating steps than in the lathe-operating steps. This shows the integrative nature of the *doing* and *knowing* steps in a given operation.

In some attempts at making an analysis for instructional purposes, the *knowing* steps of an operation have been separated from the *doing* steps and wrongly called related information. An example of such an attempt follows. It is the lathe operation again broken down, but in another way. it is impractical and is not recommended.

Lathe Operation
How to File Cylindrical Work

WHAT WORKER SHOULD DO	WHAT WORKER SHOULD KNOW
1. Select a mill file.	1. Ten inch
2. Change speed of lathe.	2. Twice turning speed
3. Proceed to file.	3. Little filing needed
4. Release pressure on return stroke.	4. Prevents forming of wire edge on serrations
5. File left handed.	5. Prevents striking dog
6. Overlap each succeeding stroke of file.	6. Necessary for smooth surfaces

The first presentation of the breakdown of this lathe operation is better. The steps are in sequence of occurrence. There is no justification for separating an operation into *doing* and *knowing* parts just for the sake of separating them, when in teaching and learning it is necessary to put them together in the integrated sequence as shown in the first illustration of the lathe operation. There is little reason for separating them on paper when they must be put together again when teaching. These items of auxiliary knowledge are inherent in an operation. They belong there. They belong with the manipulative steps and help to make the operation; they give meaning to it; the operation would not exist without the mental points or "headwork." The operating steps in an operation should be kept together in the analysis and taught by the shop teacher in sequences of occurrence whether they are manipulative or informational in nature. *Certainly the informational points, or auxiliary knowledge, should not be called information topics.*

Other attempts to identify related information by confusing the items of knowledge in an operation with related information have unfortunately resulted in the belief that the manipulative part is the actual *doing* and the related information is *knowing how* it is done. Examples taken from literature follow.

It is a waste of time and confusing to make such analyses. It suggests that there is limited experience in the practical job of teaching on the part of the persons attempting such analyses.

The points under the *doing* and *knowing* columns belong together and therefore should not be separated on paper. There

OCCUPATION OR JOB	OPERATION	DOING	KNOWING
Lathe (machine shop)	To knurl	Knurling	How to knurl
Printing	To set a line of type	Setting type	How to set type
Drafting	To draw standard threads	Drawing threads	How to draw threads
Fireman	To build a coal fire	Placing materials	How to place materials
Sulphite pulp Manufacture (acid maker)	Test the burner gas	Testing gas	How to test

is little logic in saying that "setting type" is the *doing* unit and "how to set type" is the *knowing* unit. One cannot teach the setting of type without teaching how. The *how* part of it gives existence to the operation. This sort of information should not be included under any of the three major classes of related information.

Information Topics Are Separate Assignments

Information topics, therefore, should not be created by extracting the points of integrated auxiliary knowledge from an operation and then calling them related-information topics. Information topics hold rank with operations, but they are not part of the operations. They are independent of them. The technical-information topics involve important study assignments in mathematics, science, safety education, and so on. They include any knowledge that is necessary in order to get the job done properly in a particular occupation, but they are not the mental functions of an operation. For example, in printing, "Printer's Measure" and "Kinds and Identification of Paper" are technical-information topics, but they do not appear in any of the operations. They belong in combination with operations in getting assignments done. Ten operations and three technical-information topics may be required of the printer to print a certain job.

Information topics usually do not match the operations in number; that is, there usually is not an information topic for every operation. Only occasionally is there likely to be an information topic to match an operation. In occupations composed largely of procedures for changing materials so they can be included in making products, and in service occupations, the operations predominate. Auto mechanics is one of the few occupations in which there are information topics to match practically every manipulative performance. This is because auto mechanics is largely an informational trade. Information topics in auto mechanics are likely to outnumber the operations.

A genuine information topic has its own entity as does an operation, and the nature of the occupation determines the nature and the number of information topics required. Some mass-production jobs require little if any information outside of that which is inherent in the thinking required to perform an operation.

Importance in Instruction

If a related-subjects teacher or a coordinator were to teach the *how* of an operation and the shop instructor were to teach the *doing* it is likely that there would be overlapping of responsibility and resulting confusion. The classroom teacher could not teach the *doing* without integrating the *knowing* with it. Either alone would be meaningless. One teacher would be trying to teach things that belong in the other teacher's area of instruction and get nowhere except to confuse the learners.

There are enough related topics for the related-subjects teacher or the coordinator to teach without making it necessary to include auxiliary knowledge that forms part of the operations.

The shop instructor, for example, must teach any information that belongs in an integrated way in the operations. A learner must not be sent from the print shop to another teacher to learn the *how* of the work. Such information is best presented by the shop instructor. The related-subjects teacher should limit his responsibilities to the major classifications of information and he should teach them, with any necessary elementary prerequisite instruction, in far greater detail than is possible by the shop teacher. The coordinator and supervisor should see that there is proper distribution of these responsibilities. Furthermore, they should be exceedingly well informed in analysis procedures so they can assist in making proper analyses and thus be of genuine help when they are needed in identifying teaching responsibilities.

Summary

Related-information topics are independent of the operations of an industrial occupation. Related-information topics should not be confused with the related subjects, which subjects are taught as separate courses and are designated as such in the reimbursable academic offerings under the National Vocational Education Acts. Related information in instructional analysis includes the immediate information that should be taught by the trade teacher in the shop. It should not be considered as the mental functions necessary to perform operations—the auxiliary knowledge that combines with certain manipulative steps which together constitute an operation. They are not the points of *how* and *why* and safety precautions in the operations themselves. They are major things that usually are not connected to operations. Rather, they are connected to jobs as are the operations. For example, a dozen operations and three information topics may be necessary for the production of a certain job in the print shop.

It is important that there be a clear understanding of what information topics are in order to (1) clarify and simplify the analysis assignment and (2) to clarify the teaching assignments for shop teachers and related teachers and coordinators.

There are three kinds of information topics: (1) *technical information*, (2) *general information*, and (3) *guidance information*. All form the basis for independent lessons. The technical information is that information necessary for the workman to do his work properly. It should be taught in advance of other information. General information is nice to know but not necessary. It has broadening values for the worker, but he could get along in his occupation without it. Guidance information involves choosing, preparing for, securing, holding, and making progress on a job. Vocational students need counseling and every vocational teacher should be prepared to give instruction on the foregoing points. Guidance, a whole school function, is becoming increasingly important, especially with regard to instruction on holding and making progress in one's occupation.

ASSIGNMENTS AND DISCUSSION TOPICS

1. Write a description of an information topic.
2. What are the three major kinds of information topics and why classify them? Explain and give examples of each kind. Do not use the examples given in this chapter.
3. Prepare a list of information topics for your work and classify them in three groups. This list will be used later in the final analysis of your occupation. Follow the directions in the chapter and you will have little difficulty, especially if you are well qualified in your occupation.
4. Distinguish between a point of knowledge in an operation and a real technical-information topic.
5. Explain how there may be overlapping and confusion as to responsibilities of shop and related teachers if proper distinction is not made between real information topics and points of auxiliary knowledge in operations.
6. What are the fundamental or essential elements of an occupation? Explain fully.

FOR FURTHER READING

Allen, C. R., *The Instructor, the Man, and the Job* (Philadelphia: J. B. Lippincott Co., 1919), Chaps. 7, 13, and 28.

Cushman, Frank, *Training Procedure* (New York: John Wiley and Sons, 1940), pp. 63–90.

Duenk, Lester G., "A Different Kind of Job Analysis," *The Journal of Industrial Arts Education*, Vol. 27, No. 3, Jan.–Feb., 1968, pp. 11, 12.

Giachino, J. W., and Gallington, R. O., *Course Construction in Industrial Arts and Vocational Education* (Chicago: American Technical Society, 1961).

Hoppock, Robert, *Occupational Information* (New York: McGraw-Hill Book Co., 1963).

Myers, George E., *Principles and Techniques of Vocational Guidance* (New York: McGraw-Hill Book Co., 1941), Chaps. 1 and 2.

Selvidge, R. W., *How to Teach a Trade* (Peoria: C. A. Bennett Co., 1923), Chap. 5.

Silvius, G. H., and Bohn, R. C., *Organizing Course Materials* (Bloomington, Ill.: McKnight and McKnight Publishing Co., 1961), Chaps. 7, 8, and 9.

U. S. Office of Education, *Training Bulletins in Vocational Education* (Washington, D.C.: United States Printing Office). Available in various occupations. List available. The several states also have training bulletins available.

Warters, Jane, *Techniques of Counseling* (New York: McGraw-Hill Book Co., 1964).

Making the Analysis—I

CUSTOM OCCUPATIONS

Our Knowledge Thus Far

We have learned that jobs may refer to payroll situations or to completed projects typical of the occupation under consideration. The former is a production term, and it may be used particularly when referring to training on production even though the worker actually performs operations and must be trained in them. It is job training; there is earning and learning. In occupations where custom work and high degrees of judgment forming predominate, the job is defined as a completed whole; it is a project; it may be compared to a problem in mathematics in which essential elements or fundamentals of a proper kind are combined to solve a

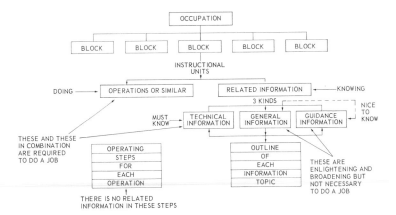

Fig. 9. *Study this graphic description of the major phases of analysis. It will help you analyze analysis.*

given problem. These elements, usually composed of operations and information topics, are necessary to make a project in the occupation.

In service occupations such as auto mechanics; radio, television, or refrigeration repair; watchmaking; and so on, a combination of essential elements is necessary to repair or overhaul a machine. The job is the repair or overhaul assignment. It is a mechanical problem that calls for solution.

The operations have little meaning when they are expressed in terms of the *using* of tools. Rather, operations should be stated in terms of performance, in terms of what is done. There is depicting, forming, shaping, or the assembling of something in an operation, and several tools, hand or machine, may be used.

Emphasis has been placed on the fact that a common difficulty in attempting analysis for instructional purposes is oversystematizing and thus making the outcome too complicated for use in training. There are many teaching and management duties that the teacher must perform without trying to follow a complicated analysis. Even teachers of long experience have difficulties in keeping an active shop functioning efficiently. The interpretation

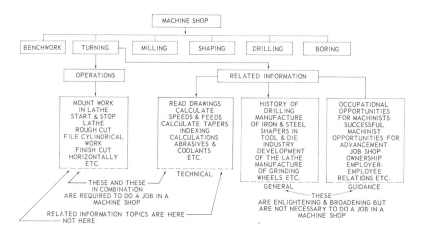

Fig. 10. *A graphic description of the major phases of analysis applied to machine shop.*

and teaching of related information can be confusing to the teacher who attempts to use an improperly made analysis of his occupation. While an occupation can be analyzed into many details, it must not be overdone; there must be simplicity.

Related-information topics are independent of operations and, therefore, should not be confused with the auxiliary knowledge that is integrated with the operations. Information topics are major units that include mathematics, science, safety education, and so on. They are topics that stand by themselves and hold rank in value and importance with the operations. There are three kinds of topics: the *technical*, which is information necessary to form judgments on the job; the *general*, which is information which is nice to know, helpful, but really not necessary; and *guidance*, which is information that should be helpful in stimulating occupational interests, choosing, preparing for, securing, holding, and making progress in an occupation. All these elements, whether they are operations or information topics, are instructional units, things to teach.

Figures 9 and 10 graphically describe the major aspects of analysis. It is now necessary to learn the next step in the analysis procedure, the way to make an order of instruction. You have already identified and listed several operations and information topics without concern as to the part of the occupation from which they came.

Blocking an Occupation

Some industrial occupations are made up of divisions of work each of which is practically an occupation in itself. That is, one can be trained in the division of the occupation and become a wage earner in it without knowing much about other divisions of that occupation. This applies to occupations in the service trades as well as to occupations in custom trades in mechanical work. These divisions are called blocks.[1] Some occupations are composed of several blocks and are called *multiblock* occupations. Others are *single block;* that is, there is only one main division. A considerable period of time may be required to learn a block in a multiblock occupation. It is not unusual to require a year or more of training to qualify for work in one block or division. Auto mechanics, machine shop, carpentry, and printing are typical occupations that are made up of several blocks varying in amount of training required in each block. In carpentry, which consists of several blocks that do not always provide independent earning opportunities after training in a particular block, it is necessary to train in most or all blocks before the learner can be placed on a job. For auto mechanics, it may be necessary only to train in a single block in order to become a wage earner.

Examples of blocks in auto mechanics, which is a service occupation are: engine repair and maintenance, electrical repair and maintenance, chassis repair and maintenance, and body repair and maintenance. These are rather distinct divisions or blocks and training in one of them would provide independent earning opportunity.

Examples of blocks in carpentry are: rough framing, roof framing, form building, stair building, window and door framing, finish carpentry, and cabinetwork. There can be some modification in these designations. Any one of them may or may not provide

1. C. R. Allen, *The Instructor, the Man, and the Job* (Philadelphia: J. B. Lippincott Co., 1919), Chap. VIII.

independent earning opportunity, depending upon the size of the organization and the number of jobs under construction. When only a few jobs are under construction at one time, or in a small organization, a carpenter is likely to be required to work in several or all blocks of the occupation. This is also true of auto mechanics.

In a large printing establishment, or in a machine shop, the blocks may be determined by the machines of the occupation. It is interesting to observe that blocking is possible even in a change-over to mass-production practices. In a large specialized production plant there can be many blocks. And, outside of production, the more complicated the occupation the more blocks there are likely to be. It should be kept in mind, however, that training requirements and not production determine whether a division of an industrial occupation is a block. Blocking is for the convenience of designating the areas of training within a complex occupation. If only a short time adjustment rather than definite training on the job is necessary to qualify for earning on a machine, as in certain semiskilled repetitive work, such work need not be identified as a block. However, as in the work of the machinist, if considerable time in weeks or months is necessary to learn the various operations on an engine lathe or on a milling machine, either of the assignments would be called blocks.

Imaginary blocks should not be set up with little or nothing to distinguish one from another. This could happen especially in single-block occupations. Unnecessary blocking merely clutters up the analysis procedure and makes it confusing. A grouping of operations in woodworking according to kinds of hand tools is an example. It serves no purpose in training. A block should be based on something tangible, something that actually sets off one part of an occupation from another and helps to simplify as well as put system into the teaching of the occupation.

There is another interpretation of blocking which has little practical use. It is the grouping of jobs or projects that are alike with respect to the elements that appear in each of them. Several similar projects are called a block. A series of such blocks is arranged from simple to complex for training purposes. Projects exactly alike, however, are difficult to find in sufficient numbers to make a series. Two different projects with the same operations and information topics can seldom be found. If they do have the same elements, they are likely to be duplicate jobs. Arrangement of projects from simple to complex can be done in an easier way, as described later in this chapter.

Importance of Blocking

What is the importance of blocking when making an instructional analysis? It is helpful in designating training areas. It is also a means of obtaining an instructional order from the simple to the complex. Each block, or division of an occupation, has operations and information topics in it that are practically all independent of the operations and information topics in other blocks. A learner, if learning a whole occupation, should move from one block to another, starting when possible with the least complex block.

Under production training conditions it is necessary to identify the blocks, but it is not always possible to rotate the learners according to the complexity of the blocks, nor to start with the least complex block. For instance, in a machine shop, the learners in a large class would be assigned to different machine areas or blocks the first day because they cannot all be given the most simple assignment. This is true in either school or plant training.

Block Base

A block base[2] is that part of an occupation which has instructional elements or certain other characteristics common to all blocks and which must be included in the training of a learner of any block or division of the occupation. For instance, certain bench and layout operations are common to most blocks of the work of the machinist and may be taught to all the learners of the occupation or parts of the occupation.

Other characteristics that determine block bases are commonness of materials, or machines, or production necessity, or anything that ties various blocks of an occupation together; these all learners must know and be able to do in all blocks.

Block bases as well as blocks are sometimes more imaginary

2. *Ibid.*, pp. 68–72.

than real.[3] When blocks and block bases are hard to recognize there is oversystematizing and resulting confusion. The beginning teacher gets into difficulties by trying to follow the system instead of teaching. The blocks should be clearly set apart as divisions of the occupation, and block bases should be the common training elements of the blocks. A charting device, described in this chapter, simplifies detection of any common learning situations involved in an occupation, and if they exist, they are clearly visible.

Importance of a Block Base

The advantage of knowing the block base of a multiblock occupation is that it helps to secure economy and effectiveness of instruction. It identifies the instruction that must be given all learners in all blocks of the occupation. It is the common necessary basic instruction. For instance, in wood patternmaking the block base would include the common woodworking operations and information that a learner in patternmaking requires to continue the learning of all the blocks. The blocks in patternmaking would be designated by types of patterns, such as solid patterns, built-up patterns, cored patterns, and so on.

Arranging the Essential Elements in a Custom Occupation

The next step in making an analysis of a custom production occupation is to continue making the list of instructional units for the occupation or block of the occupation that you have already started by checking them in typical work jobs. A relative order of instruction of operations can now be determined, and a progressive order of jobs from the simple to the more complex ones can be arranged by means of a simple charting procedure.

The charting procedure is one of the most valuable techniques that has come into analysis procedures since its early inception. It has simplified the making of the analysis, and it affords a graphic procedure for securing an instructional order by inspection. It is more practical and positive and easier than were the earlier attempts to arrange an instructional order by grouping

3. *Ibid.*, p. 110.

cards, studying them separately, and shuffling them with the hope of working out an instructional order. This requires a good deal of visualizing and guessing.

The charting technique makes it practically unnecessary to be concerned about the problem of blocking jobs for progression. That is, it is unnecessary to attempt to group several jobs with the same elements in each. Moreover, it is seldom that two different jobs with exactly the same operations can be found. When the chart is used, learning progression is obtained anyway. One needs only to take the division of an occupation or block, or the whole occupation under consideration, and chart it as in Figures 11 and 12 to discover the operations and typical jobs in a progressive instructional order for training purposes. See Figure 17 for the method used in charting a service occupation.

The making of a chart in analyzing a custom occupation is based on blocks or divisions of the occupation, or on a whole occupation when there is only one block in the occupation. That is, a chart may be used to analyze one block, a block being a division set off rather distinctly from other divisions. For example, a chart should be made for analyzing engine-lathe work in a machine shop, or composition work or linotype work in the print shop. It would be more difficult to use the charting procedure for a multiblock trade than for a single-block occupation or a block alone. Some multiblock occupations like carpentry can be charted without making the chart too large. Judgment is needed as to the practicability of charting all of a multiblock occupation on one paper. A rather large chart would be required for a multiblock occupation like the machinist trade, but it would not be helpful. A separate small chart is convenient to work with and is usually made for one block such as for milling-machine work.

Examine Figure 11 and sketch a layout for a chart similar to the one shown. This can be done on any kind of paper without at first being concerned about the size. If you want to work to a size at the outset, see the Appendix for a satisfactory, proved layout. On the left side, list the operations.[4] This list was started when you studied Chapter 4 and carried out the assignments. A list of jobs or projects was also started. Across the top of the

4. They may not be called operations in your occupation, but nevertheless they are things you do.

ANALYSIS OF JOBS IN GAS-WELDING

Columns (TYPICAL JOBS): SPINDLE HOOK · TANK WRENCH – SP. · VAT – 16 GAUGE · FIRE SHIELD · A-C BRACE – 8 GAUGE · MITER CHANNEL – 90° · ANGLE CHANNEL – 90° · PIPE TEE · FLUX BOX – 16 GAUGE · TRUCK WHEEL · FILLER-ROD HOLDER · BROKEN SPOKE · BUILD UP SHAFT · TEST ROD · TEST PIPE · PIPE ELL · FLOOR LAMP · PIPE Y · PIPE REDUCER · TRACK SUPPORT · C.I. GEAR TOOTH · V-BLOCK JIG · BUILD UP LUG · REPAIR CAST IRON · SQUARE FRAME · FRAME SCHEDULE · TRAY SUPPORT

Rows (OPERATIONS): SET UP EQUIPMENT · CUT STEEL PLATE · SELECT AND ADJUST TIP · ADJUST FLAME · CUT HEAVY ROD AND BAR · MAKE A WELD – NO ROD · MAKE A BEAD WELD – 45° · MAKE A BEAD WELD – 90° · LAY OUT WITH TEMPLATE · MAKE WELD – ROD ANY POSITION · TAKE OUT STRAIN IN CASTING · TRIM-CUT A STRAIGHT EDGE · BUTT-WELD ANGLE AND CHANNEL · START FOUNDATION · LAP-WELD THICK STEEL · CUT PIPE AND TUBING · WELD PIPE AND TUBING · HEAT FOR EXPANSION · BUILD UP WELD · MAKE WELD – ROD HORIZONTAL · LAY OUT WITHOUT TEMPLATE · WELD CAST IRON · FASTEN WITH CLAMPS · CUT A BEVEL EDGE · ANNEAL · BRAZE · WELD ALUMINUM · DESIGN AND FINISH

Fig. 11. *Securing an instructional order.*

ANALYSIS OF JOBS IN GAS-WELDING

OPERATIONS / TYPICAL JOBS	1 SPINDLE HOOK	2 FLUX BOX – 16 GUAGE	3 VAT – 16 GUAGE	4 FIRE SHIELD	5 A-C BRACE – 8 GUAGE	6 MITER CHANNEL – 90o	7 ANGLE CHANNEL – 90o	8 FRAME SCHEDULE	9 TANK WRENCH – SP.	10 V-BLOCK JIG	11 BUILD UP SHAFT	12 TEST ROD	13 PIPE ELL	14 PIPE TEE	15 PIPE Y	16 PIPE REDUCER	17 FILLER-ROD HOLDER	18 TEST PIPE	19 TRUCK WHEEL	20 TRACK SUPPORT	21 C.I. GEAR TOOTH	22 BROKEN SPOKE	23 BUILD UP LUG	24 REPAIR CAST IRON	25 SQUARE FRAME	26 FLOOR LAMP	27 TRAY STAND
1 SET UP EQUIPMENT	1	1	1	1	1	1	1	1	1	1	1	1	1	1	1	1	1	1	1	1	1	1	1	1	1	1	1
2 SELECT AND ADJUST TIP	2	2	2	2	2	2	2	2	2	2	2	2	2	2	2	2	2	2	2	2	2	2	2	2	2	2	2
3 ADJUST FLAME	3	3	3	3	3	3	3	3	3	3	3	3	3	3	3	3	3	3	3	3	3	3	3	3	3	3	3
4 START FOUNDATION	4	4	4	4	4	4	4	4	4	4	4	4	4	4	4	4	4	4	4	4	4	4	4	4	4	4	4
5 DESIGN AND FINISH	5	5	5	5	5	5	5	5	5	5	5	5	5	5	5	5	5	5	5	5	5	5	5	5	5	5	5
6 MAKE A WELD – NO ROD		6	6	6			6	6	6	6	6	6	6	6	6	6	6	6	6	6	6	6	6	6	6	6	6
7 MAKE A BEAD WELD – 45o	7	7	7				7	7		7	7	7	7	7	7	7	7	7	7	7	7	7	7	7	7	7	7
8 MAKE A BEAD WELD – 90o		8	8	8			8	8	8	8	8	8	8	8	8	8	8	8	8	8	8	8	8	8	8	8	8
9 MAKE WELD – ROD ANY POSITION							9	9	9	9	9	9	9	9	9	9	9	9	9		9	9	9	9	9	9	9
10 MAKE WELD – ROD HORIZONTAL				10			10	10	10	10	10	10	10	10	10	10	10	10			10	10	10	10	10	10	10
11 CUT STEEL PLATE				11					11	11							11		11							11	11
12 CUT BEVEL EDGE					12	12	12	12	12	12									12	12		12		12	12		
13 TRIM-CUT A STRAIGHT EDGE						13	13	13	13	13		13	13	13	13	13	13	13	13	13	13			13		13	13
14 BUTT-WELD ANGLE & CHANNEL						14	14	14	14	14							14		14	14					14		
15 CUT HEAVY ROD AND BAR									15	15		15							15			15		15	16	15	15
16 LAP-WELD THICK STEEL									16	16		16							16	16							
17 CUT PIPE AND TUBING										17			17	17	17	17	17	17	17							17	17
18 WELD PIPE AND TUBING										18			18	18	18	18	18	18	18							18	18
19 HEAT FOR EXPANSION								19			19									19	19	19	20	19	19		
20 BUILD UP WELD											20										20	20	20			20	20
21 LAY OUT WITH TEMPLATE														21	21	21									21	21	22
22 LAY OUT WITHOUT TEMPLATE																	22	22	22							22	22
23 WELD CAST IRON																					23	23	23	23			
24 FASTEN WITH CLAMPS																				24		24		24	24	24	24
25 TAKE OUT STRAIN IN CASTING																					25	25		25	25	25	
26 ANNEAL																								26	26		
27 BRAZE																					27	27				27	27
28 WELD ALUMINUM																										28	28

Fig. 12. *Securing an instructional order.*

chart, write first the names of what you believe to be the simple projects. It is not necessary at the outset to arrange the operations according to any particular order. However, it will be helpful later if you begin by listing those that you now know to be simple and frequently used. Do not be concerned if you do not seem to have all of them. Continue by listing all the operations you can, even those that do not seem to be used very often.

Examine the jobs one at a time to see what operations appear in each and check them as in Figure 11. Place the check marks in the squares that form the columns under the jobs. As you study the jobs further you will think of operations that you have not yet listed. Add them to the list of operations and continue to check the jobs in which they appear. Add jobs at the same time while you continue to extend the operation list. By the time you have listed 25 or more jobs across the top you should also have a rather complete list of operations on the left side of the chart. This depends on the occupation. Some occupations, such as tailoring, do not have many typical jobs. Even though you may have started the list of operations in Chapter 4, you may not have listed all operations. Several days may pass before the list is fairly complete.

As you examine the jobs for the operations that are in them you should also think of technical-information topics that are necessary. Remember that the information topics are not the items of auxiliary knowledge which give meaning to an operation. There will be independent topics relating to science, mathematics, safety education, and so on, depending on the occupation. You may either list these topics below the operations on the chart or on separate paper. As you proceed you will discover that only the technical topics can be listed and checked on the chart. General and guidance topics are more difficult to check because of their general nature. Follow carefully again, if necessary, the discussion on information topics in Chapter 5.

When making an analysis, it is helpful to consult books and drawings and other available materials. There is much material that will be of help in making an analysis of an occupation. A very helpful procedure also is to work at jobs. Many operations will then come to mind. *Remember that a mere listing of tools or equipment in terms of use is not enough.* Anyone can do that without knowing anything about the occupation and the list would be of no value. The operations in a production occupation should be stated in terms of depicting something, forming or shaping of materials, or assembling of parts.

Arranging an Instructional Order

Examine the whole chart in Figure 11. Observe whether there are any full rows of check marks (rows are horizontal). Keep in mind that the check marks represent the operations. Examine the columns (vertical) and observe that they differ with respect to the number of check marks in each. Transfer the names of all operations that have full rows of check marks to the top of the list in Figures 11 and 12. These operations appear in all jobs and are frequently used and must therefore be taught first. They form a basis for the remaining work without which the learner cannot proceed. If you have analyzed a block in an occupation, the units represented in the solidly checked rows across the top of the sheet may be the block base. This is true in occupations where the block base is composed of common instructional elements. If a chart were made for patternmaking, for example, the block base would be the common woodworking operations that appear in all jobs and such operations would have solid rows of check marks after them. This brings out another advantage of the charting technique.

It is not important whether you think the operations represented in these solid rows are easy or difficult; that is a matter of individual differences. Some things that are difficult for some persons are easy for others. Easy or difficult, the most frequently used operations, the basic ones, must be taught first so the learner will have a foundation for the operations to follow. It is much like mathematics. Common arithmetic operations, which vary in difficulty with persons learning them, are taught first because they appear frequently in all mathematics to follow.

There will be auxiliary operations that cannot be checked readily against the jobs. Examples of auxiliary operations, referred to in Chapter 4, are "sharpen edge tools," "dress a grinding wheel," "dress a screwdriver," and so on. There is choice as to whether to place the auxiliary operations at the end of the list and not check them, or to place them at the top with the frequently used operations. If placed at the top, they should be given check marks.

Since it is necessary in training to go from the simple to the complex, the jobs with a few operations in them are made first, then more complex ones, and so on. Therefore, examine the columns to see that those at the left are short and those toward the right become continuously longer. If necessary, shift the jobs until the columns increase in length, proceeding from left to right. That is, the first column on the left should be the shortest and the farthest column on the right should be the longest. The columns should increase gradually in length, or in number of check marks, from left to right. A good arrangement is shown in Figure 12. The longer the list and the greater the variety of jobs, the greater is the possibility of obtaining an imaginary diagonal line across the bottom of the columns, such as suggested at A in Figure 12. This line is easy to discover. It is not highly important and it should not be included in completing the chart. It serves merely as a guide that shows whether the columns are increasing in length from left to right. However, be sure that the most frequently used operations appear first, then the next most frequently used ones, and so on. This is indicated by the check marks in the rows. The top rows should be solid with check marks. The number of solid rows depends on the occupation or block of the occupation being analyzed.

After you have rearranged the chart so the most frequently used operations are at the top of the list, and the jobs are arranged across the top of the chart from left to right in order from the simple to the complex, your experience and judgment will help in placing the less frequently used operations as you continue down the list. The last operations are the least used ones as well as the ones that appear in the more complex jobs. There are likely to be a few scattered check marks that do not follow the imaginary diagonal line, but that is not important. However, it is important to place the solid rows of check marks at the top with the less solid rows next, continuing with the least checked rows toward the bottom.

Number the Operations

When the operations and jobs have been rearranged so that the most frequently used operations appear first in the list on the left side of the chart, and the jobs are in order at the top from the simple to the more complex going from left to right, the operations are then ready to be numbered from the top to the bottom beginning with number *one* as in Figure 12. After the operations that are named at the left have been numbered, replace all check marks in the rows with numbers that correspond to the numbers of the operations shown in Figure 12. For example, in every square with a check mark opposite operation 4, replace the check mark with number 4. Then, after you have replaced all check marks with numbers, as you read down the column under any given job or project, you will have the numbers of the operations in that job. Also, you will have an approximate teaching order of operations and an arrangement of typical jobs that will assist you in proceeding from the simple to the complex in the jobs that are selected. There is a progressive order of jobs. This procedure does away with any need for the blocking of jobs for progression. If you prepare operation sheets or visual aids, they should be given the numbers already assigned the operations on the chart.

If the technical information topics are placed on the chart, they should be put at the bottom below the operations, each topic given a letter in the column rather than a number. This would reserve the numbers for the operations and make them easy to identify. Be sure, however, that you do not list auxiliary items of knowledge from the questions in your desire to make a long list of topics. There usually are many more operations than information topics. Of course, you can also include general and guidance information topics, but their locations will not be specific as are the operations and technical topics.

If you do choose to place the information topics on the chart below the operations, it will be necessary to change the heading "operations" at the top of the column to "instructional units."

The chart should not be regarded as the analysis itself, although many teachers appreciate its value and put it in permanent form. It is a device for expediting the analysis procedure. It can be put in permanent form by making a tracing and then blue or black-and-white prints. A suitable form for a chart is shown in the Appendix. After the chart is completed, the list of operations should be transferred to cards and each operation further analyzed into steps. This is explained in Chapter 7. The value of the charting procedure is in listing operations by checking them under the jobs and in arranging a relative instructional order. It is the most effective device available for arranging jobs of a custom occupation in a progressive order from simple to complex. It is more convenient than shuffling cards in an attempt to secure an instructional order.

So long as people differ in learning ability, it will always be difficult to predict in advance an *exact* order for operations beyond the most frequently used ones which should appear at the top of the chart. These are certain of first place in a teaching order.

The jobs listed at the top are not assumed to be the ones that must be made. They are merely typical and were only used in making the chart. There can be choice of jobs not on the list, but care should be taken to check the units to make sure that they belong. The jobs on this chart, it should be emphasized, were merely chosen as *typical* of those that are produced in your shop. They enable you to more readily identify and check the operations and distinguish the operations from the jobs in your occupation.

Frequency, Complexity, and Difficulty As Factors in Securing an Instructional Order

Despite the fact that the difficulty is often thought to be the factor that determines the teaching order, an elementary understanding of individual differences, and an examination of the analysis chart, will convince one that frequency of use of operations determines their teaching order. Complexity and not difficulty determines the order of jobs or projects. Difficulty is a human consideration that varies with individuals. Many simple tasks are difficult for some people and many complex tasks are rather easy for others. The arrangement of jobs across the top of the chart from simple to complex assures progress in a series in which each part is in a progressive order. Of course, if a complex job is undertaken before more simple ones, difficulty becomes a matter of individual differences. Advanced work based on thorough basic training may be comparatively easy for many learners. By making a chart and placing the frequently used operations at the top of the sheet, identification of the needed basic preparation for the more advanced work is assured.

Rearranging Cards

Shuffling the cards shown in Figure 16 is less accurate than the chart method for determining instructional order. A good deal of imagination and guessing are involved in rearranging cards, whereas the chart shows the order at a glance. The chart establishes the order for the cards before they are made, and the numbers for the cards are taken from the chart.

Progression Factors

The conditions that determine an instructional order of operations and arrangement of jobs so that progress is certain in learning a trade are called progression factors.[5] Simple basic things must be taught first; if too many learning points must be covered by a learner early, and at one time, he is likely to be confused. Learning is hindered and there is an increased possibility of accidents.

In practically all industrial occupations, *frequency of use* of operations and arrangement of jobs from *simple to complex* are the usual progression factors. To repeat an oft-made statement supported by psychology, learning difficulty is not a factor that determines an instructional order. People differ in so many things which they try to learn and do that difficulty becomes an individual thing. One cannot determine in advance what difficulty may develop.

Frequency of use of operations and complexity of jobs are constant factors; they affect all learners. The charting technique does away with the older laborious way of determining progression factors. Read down the chart for operations and to the right for jobs, and thus determine whether the instructional material is likely to lead to a gradual full learning of the occupation or block.

There must be an increase from a low degree to a high degree

5. Allen, *op. cit.*, pp. 80–84.

of *accuracy, speed,* and *confidence* as one progresses in learning an occupation, all of which should come with good instruction and good instructional conditions. Speed and accuracy can be developed together. However, there are differences of opinion regarding this point. Many experienced teachers believe that accuracy should be stressed first and speed will come. Learners do not always give their maximum in speed; a good way to develop it is to instill the idea of speed at the start. It is an important human asset in industry and it goes hand in hand with accuracy. As these develop, confidence is likely also to grow. These must become deeply fixed habits. The teaching process is largely a matter of habit building. As the proper habits in shopwork are established, accuracy, speed, and confidence should be present. They are points that should be observed in all instruction.

Checking Levels

There frequently is need in teaching an occupation for predetermined places at which a learner must be checked to see that he is making progress. The conditions and situations that determine checking levels vary in all occupations. The levels are determined when making the analysis, and, of course, it is largely a matter of judgment because a teacher can seldom tell in advance where and when he must check on the expected attainment. Checking levels are really psychological rather than mechanical.

Allen[6] established certain levels of attainment according to degrees of advancement that should be expected of a learner at certain stages of learning. These levels are made to fit a particular occupation. They are diagramed for ready interpretation in Figure 13. They are: Level I—work that can be expected of a new or "green" learner. In such cases there is possibility of accidents, waste of material, improper use of tools or equipment. Level II—work that can be expected of a learner who should be doing work a step above Level I, a worker partly trained. Level III—work included in this level when mastered should indicate that the learner is about half trained. Level IV—work in this level when mastered should indicate a rather well-trained person. Level V—ability to do work which is predetermined for this level

6. *Ibid.,* pp. 83, 89.

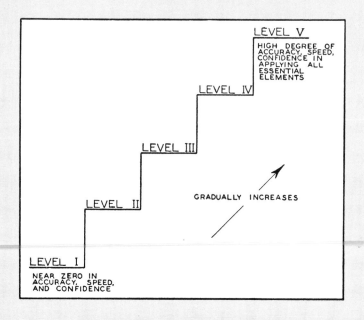

Fig. 13. *Levels of attainment in learning an occupation.*

should indicate that the learner can perform any operation, knows all necessary information topics thoroughly, and can do most any job in the technical occupation being taught. There should be less possibility of accidents, no waste of materials, and skillful performance of operations.

As the learner advances, he should be improving in rate of accuracy, speed, and confidence and these must be checked as he progresses. These checking level specifications are only suggestive and relative according to Allen.[7] Many years of experience have shown that the charting technique, Figures 11 and 12, reduces guessing and simplifies the making of checking levels. Making checking levels is a matter of judgment determined by experience. They can be arranged on the chart, and then all that is necessary is to check or draw heavy lines across the chart at intervals of a

7. *Ibid.*, Chap. X.

certain number of operations and down the chart at job intervals that are decided upon as places to check progress. There is no assurance, however, that progress will be made just because checking levels are established. The important thing to know and to watch for in teaching is to see that accuracy, speed, and confidence have been mastered to the high level that is required and can be expected of a learner as he advances in the occupation. This is one of the fundamentals of teaching that must be mastered by an instructor. There is no short cut to mastering this procedure; constant and persistent effort on the part of the teacher are required.

Predetermined checking levels are difficult to follow and to keep in mind while teaching an active and busy class because of individual differences in the rate and quality of the learner's achievement, and because of management problems. Each operation should be a checking level. If an instructor uses the chart, Figure 12, and sees to it that the learners are gradually mastering the operations at the left and working on jobs typical of those at the top that are selected from the left to right of the chart, and if the learners are watched to see that they are gaining in accuracy, speed, and confidence, there will be little need for concern about establishing checking levels. The charting technique simplifies all the earlier difficulties of setting up checking levels by means of shuffling cards, and it is therefore less difficult for a beginning teacher to follow. The chart is visible and makes inspection and recording a rather simple task. It is easier to see and compare all parts of an occupation or division of it on a chart than it is to arrange and rearrange cards containing descriptions of parts of it. If, however, the chart is not used, a card system should be employed and checking levels created by grouping the cards according to the five levels suggested by Allen.

Recording Progress

A record must be kept of the progress of each learner in vocational-technical training. A busy instructor cannot hope to keep in mind the status of progress of every member of a class. There are many teaching and management duties that prevent this. The simplest way to keep a record of progress is to make use of the analysis chart, Figure 12. By substituting the names of the learners for the names of the jobs across the top of the chart and by leaving out the check marks, progress can be checked in the columns for each operation and information topic. Charts containing only the names of the operations and information topics can be made up in quantities from a tracing or by duplicating as shown in Figure 14. The instructor must have a system of marks to indicate what progress the learner is making. A common method is to use the three numerals 1, 2, and 3. If a learner is just barely achieving on an operation, numeral *one* is placed under his name and after the unit in question. When he improves in accuracy, speed, and confidence to what would be average ability, or about Level III in Figure 13, numeral *two* replaces numeral *one* on the chart. When he has attained the highest degree of ability in speed, accuracy, and confidence that can be expected, Level V, then numeral *three* replaces number *two*. It is not necessary to attempt to use numerals 1, 3, and 5 to correspond to Levels I, III, and V and it is not necessary to attempt to use numerals representing all five levels. It refines the checking too much and is unnecessary. Two numerals would be even more practical than five.

On first thought, recording of progress on a chart according to units of instruction appears to be a difficult task. Progress must be recorded, however, and the recording should be based on mastery of fundamentals. The learner should be checked on his ability to do what the instructor has taught him. Merely checking completed projects or major work assignments to see how they look when completed does not tell whether the learner mastered all the elements involved. He may have worked in a crude manner when the instructor was not looking. It is the instructor's duty to follow up and move from learner to learner to see that he is performing the operation in the manner in which he was instructed. He must correct any faults in doing the operation. When the learner has performed it as well as can be expected on his first attempt, he should then be checked on the chart with numeral *one* for that operation. As the learner improves, the record should be changed.

The instructor must develop a technique for recording the progress of his class. He must be in command of certain fundamentals as is the learner. Recording progress is one of the fundamentals

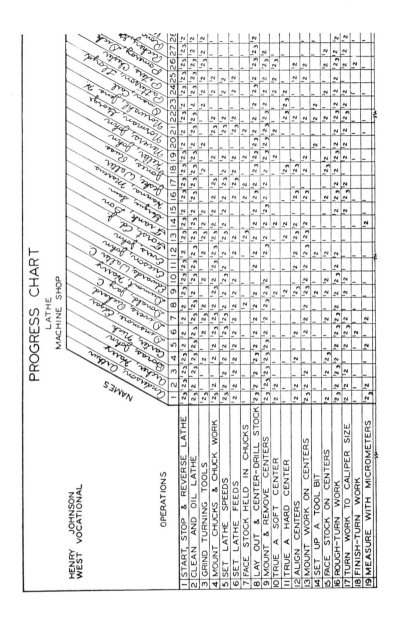

Fig. 14. *Progress chart.*

of teaching that he must learn. It is not difficult, however, if he learns to carry the status of several learners in mind and records them at one time. It is not necessary, as one may at first assume, to shuttle back and forth for each operation from learner to record chart. The recording technique becomes a simple procedure as does the performance of an operation by a highly skilled workman. The new teacher, too, must develop accuracy, speed, and confidence in instructing and managing.

Experience has shown that when the record chart is posted so all can see it, it has the effect of inspiring improvement. It is natural for learners to want to excel, and posting the record publicly tends to inspire them to do so. The objectives of a course should be the guide in determining whether detailed checking of achievement is desirable or necessary in industrial arts.

SERVICE OCCUPATIONS

In the foregoing section, the charting technique was described for use in analyzing occupations in which objects are produced. Service occupations—occupations that involve the repair, overhauling, or installation of machines, such as auto, refrigerator, radio, television, telephone, airplane, and so on—are not readily charted by means of this technique. All details as to operations such as blocking apply to service as well as to other industrial occupations, so they should be studied carefully. However, jobs that involve the making of something are practically nonexistent in service occupations. Inasmuch as articles are not produced but repairs are made to an existing machine, the top row of jobs or projects shown in Figure 12 cannot be supplied in making a similar chart for a service occupation. A repair, overhaul, or installation assignment is comparable to a problem in arithmetic, as is the project or job in a custom trade. It is necessary for the skilled workman to study a given situation, diagnose the trouble, and bring into play a combination of essential elements that will overcome the difficulty, solve the problem.

Standard Elements of Procedure

Ocassionally it is difficult to make distinctions between operations and jobs in service occupations. It is more important to recognize that there are certain standard elements of procedure that must be taught to a learner. There are elements of procedure that singly or in combination are brought into use in a repair or overhaul assignment. The majority of them are of disassembly and assembly nature. Depicting, shaping, and forming operations seldom appear. The term *instructional unit* applies in designating the elements of procedure, whether they are of *doing* or of *knowing* kind, and whether there is doubt as to their identification as operations or as jobs. If they constitute lessons to be taught, they are instructional units. You would be right if you called all the elements *instructional units*, even in industrial occupations, because that is what they are. You need not be concerned whether they should be called operations.

The many work situations of a service operation could be listed and put on a chart in the place provided for jobs in a custom occupation, as shown in Figure 12, but it takes considerable description to identify them. It would be necessary to describe each work assignment by means of a brief job description. Jobs in custom occupations are more readily identified; they need only be named; they are quite tangible. Charts for making an analysis of a custom occupation are usable in analyzing service occupations, however, if care is given to describing the jobs. It has been done with satisfaction many times.

Two-Column Chart

A good way to list the elements of a service occupation is to make a two-column chart. One column would include the operations and the other the information topics. Anticipated repair or overhaul assignments need not be listed. An example of such an arrangement is shown in Figure 15.

On the left side are listed the manipulative elements; on the right side the information topics. First, on the right, the technical information topics can be listed, below them the general and guidance topics as one chooses to arrange them, or in order of seeming importance.

B-10.   CLUTCH ASSEMBLY

	DOING		KNOWING
1	ADJUST CLUTCH PEDAL	1	CONSTRUCTION AND OPERATION OF THE CLUTCH
2	ADJUST CLUTCH FINGERS	2	CLUTCH FAILURES
3	DISASSEMBLE AND ASSEMBLE CLUTCH	3	CLUTCH BRAKE
4	OVERHAUL THE CLUTCH	4	CLUTCH BALANCE
5	CHECK CLUTCH SPRING TENSION	5	PEDAL CLEARANCE
6	CLEAN CLUTCH PARTS	6	TYPES OF CLUTCH FACINGS
7	REMOVE AND INSTALL THE CLUTCH HUB		
8	REMOVE AND INSTALL THE CLUTCH HUB BEARING		
9	RE-LINE THE CLUTCH		
10	FIT AND ALIGN CLUTCH THROW-OUT YOKE		

B-11.   CARBURETOR

	DOING		KNOWING
1	REMOVE AND INSTALL THE CARBURETOR	1	CARBURETION
2	DISASSEMBLE AND ASSEMBLE THE CARBURETOR	2	PRINCIPLES OF THE INTERNAL COMBUSTION ENGINES
3	TRACE PATHS OF AIR AND GASOLINE		
4	CHECK AND ADJUST FLOAT LEVEL	3	CAUSES OF ABNORMAL EXHAUST COLOR
5	CLEAN FUEL SCREENS, FUEL LINES AND TANKS	4	RATIOS AND EFFECTS OF FUEL-AIR MIXTURES
6	ADJUST IDLING MIXTURE	5	EFFECTS OF COMPRESSION
7	FIT THE THROTTLE VALVE BODY AND MAIN BODY	6	INTACT MANIFOLDS
8	INSTALL NEW JET GASKETS	7	THEORY OF CARBURETION
9	ADJUST ECONOMIZER JET TO THROTTLE VALVE	8	CARBURETOR TROUBLES AND REMEDIES
10	INSTALL AIR HORN	9	FLOAT LEVELS AND CHECKING

B-12.   LUBRICATION

	DOING		KNOWING
1	LOCATE FITTINGS	1	READ LUBRICANT CHART
2	WIPE OFF GREASE FITTINGS	2	GRADES OF LUBRICANTS
3	FORCE GREASE WITH PRESSURE GUN	3	AMOUNTS OF LUBRICANTS
4	LUBRICATE THE TANK THOROUGHLY	4	FLUSHING OIL
5	CHANGE ENGINE OIL		
6	CHANGE TRANSMISSION AND DIFFERENTIAL LUBRICANT		
7	CHANGE FINAL DRIVE LUBRICANT		
8	CHANGE OIL IN AIR CLEANERS		
9	FLUSH THE ENGINE OIL TANK		
10	FLUSH THE TRANSMISSION AND DIFFERENTIAL		

Fig. 15. *Section of two-column chart.*

Even though the columns are side by side, the information topics need not match the operations one by one. This would only happen by chance. Auto mechanics, however, is a service occupation that has as many information topics as operations, if not more, and many of the topics match the operations. Auto mechanics is an assembly and technical information occupation and requires a large number of technical information topics.

A satisfactory way to identify the column that includes the manipulative elements is to head it with the word *doing* and the column with the information topics with the word *knowing*. Both columns include instructional units.

Analysis Procedures Are Alike

The service occupations, when analyzed, should be blocked the same as custom occupations. All the blocks can be laid out on one chart without making it unduly large as is shown by the section taken from a larger chart, Figure 15. There are multiblock service occupations, like auto mechanics, just as there are multiblock custom occupations. The major difference to consider is the fact, already mentioned, that objects are serviced, repaired, or overhauled in the service occupations, whereas objects are produced or made in the custom occupations. Otherwise the analysis procedures for both classes of occupations are alike.

The procedure for recording achievements by means of charts, Chapter 12, is advisable in all vocational-technical training. The method of listing the instructional or operating steps as described in the next chapter applies in all occupations. After the doing and knowing units have been discovered, they should be broken down into steps in the same way and for the same reason as in custom occupations. The next assignment in analyzing an occupation, then, is to break down the instructional units into instructional steps as explained in the next chapter. It is desirable, in any occupation or activity being analyzed, to break down the instructional units into steps so as to be sure that all points are covered in the teaching.

Summary

Some occupations are made up of several divisions. They are of such nature that a worker can be trained and become a wage earner in one of them without knowing much about the other divisions. These divisions are called *blocks*. Occupations that are composed of several blocks are called *multiblock* occupations. The more complex the occupation, the more blocks there are likely to be. Training, and not production requirements, determines the blocks. Considerable time is usually required to train a person in one block.

Blocks should not be set up just to have them. If major training areas are not designated, blocking should not be attempted. A block should have instructional units in it that are practically independent of units in other blocks. If all of a multiblock occupation is to be learned, the student should start with the least complex block.

A *block base* identifies the instructional elements that are common to all blocks and which should be taught all learners of a multiblock occupation.

A relative order of instruction of operations and a progressive order of jobs or projects in a block can be arranged by means of a charting procedure. It simplifies the making of the analysis and affords a graphic procedure for securing an instructional order by inspection as shown in Figure 12. The most frequently used operations must be taught first. Difficulty does not determine the order of teaching the instructional units. Jobs are arranged in order from the simple to the complex. These are progression factors and are determined by the charting procedure. In achievement there must be an increase from a low degree to a high degree of accuracy, speed, and confidence. As the proper habits in shopwork are developed there is an increase in accuracy, speed, and confidence.

Frequently, there is need for having predetermined places at which a learner should be checked to see that he is making progress. As the student progresses, there should be less possibility of accidents, less waste of materials, and proper use of tools and equipment. Predetermined checking places are called checking levels; they are determined by judgment and experience. The charting procedure simplifies the problem of determining checking levels. Each instructional unit is a natural checking level.

A record should be kept of the progress of each learner, because the teacher cannot hope to keep in mind the records of progress for the whole class. The analysis chart makes a simple record of progress. The names of the jobs can be replaced by the names of the learners as in Figure 14. Recording should be based on mastery of fundamental elements; therefore, the value of the chart. The teacher must learn the technique for checking. He must be in command of certain fundamentals in teaching and management, and one of these is to learn the method of recording progress. He must develop accuracy, speed, and confidence in this and many other teaching duties if he is to be a successful teacher.

It is desirable to make a two-column chart in listing the instructional units of service occupations. The chart described for making an analysis of a custom occupation is difficult to use in the analysis of a service occupation because the jobs are not as tangible in the latter as in the former. The repair assignments are assumed and not designated in the two-column charts. One column includes the *doing* units and the other the *knowing* units. This kind of arrangement permits an analysis of all blocks of an occupation on one chart.

ASSIGNMENTS AND DISCUSSION TOPICS

1. What is a block and of what value is it in analyzing an occupation?
2. Explain the meaning of jobs, operations, and information topics in industrial occupations.
3. Identify and list the blocks in your occupation if it is a multi-block custom occupation, and pass them to your instructor for approval. If you are analyzing a single-block occupation, this will not be necessary.
4. Continue to analyze your occupation, but do one block at a time if it is a multiblock occupation.
5. Select the block that you will analyze first, if it is a custom occupation, and on a large piece of paper, sketch a chart. List the operations and jobs in it in the manner suggested in this chapter. Check the operations in each job. Present this for the approval of your instructor.

6. After your chart has been approved, replace the check marks with numbers. Complete the chart by supplying all data according to the form in the Appendix.
7. If you desire a chart in permanent form like a blueprint, you may arrange to have it done by a draftsman.
8. Name some elements that help a teacher to determine the instructional order of any group of operations and jobs in a custom occupation.
9. If your occupation is a multiblock service occupation, list the blocks and arrange them on a two-column chart. Have them approved by your instructor.
10. List the operations and information topics of your occupation on the two-column chart.
11. Can you place all blocks on one chart?
12. Can all the blocks of a custom occupation be conveniently analyzed on a chart of the kind described in Chapter 6?
13. Are doing elements in a service occupation likely to be similar in kind to the doing elements in a custom occupation? That is, are there depicting, forming, shaping, and assembling operations? Which kind is likely to be greatest in number in a service occupation?
14. Distinguish jobs in a service occupation from jobs in a custom occupation.

FOR FURTHER READING

Allen, C. R., *The Instructor, the Man, and the Job* (Philadelphia: J. B. Lippincott Co., 1919), Chaps. 8–14.

Broadbent, V. E., "Improved Check-off Record," *Industrial Arts and Vocational Education*, Vol. 54, No. 2, February, 1965, pp. 40–44.

Cushman, Frank, *Training Procedure* (New York: John Wiley and Sons, 1940), pp. 63–90.

Giachino, J. W., and Gallington, R. O., *Course Construction in Industrial Arts and Vocational Education* (Chicago: American Technical Society, 1961).

Rudiger, E. R., "Teaching Motor Skills in Depth in Vocational Areas," *Industrial Arts and Vocational Education*, Vol. 54, No.2, February, 1965, pp. 29, 30.

Selvidge, R. W., *How to Teach a Trade* (Peoria: C. A. Bennett Co., 1923), Chaps. 4, 5, 10.

Selvidge, R. W., and Fryklund, V. C., *Principles of Trade and Industrial Teaching* (Peoria: C. A. Bennett Co., 1946), Chaps. 4, 5.

Silvius, G. H., and Bohn, R. C., *Organizing Course Materials* (Bloomington, Ill.: McKnight and McKnight Publishing Co.), Chaps. 7, 8, 9.

U. S. Office of Education, *Training Bulletins in Vocational Education* (Washington, D.C.: United States Printing Office). Available in various occupations. List is available.

Bulletins covering analyses of trades are available in most Divisions of Vocational Education in the various State Departments of Education. Obtain these from your state.

7

Making the Analysis—II

LISTING THE INSTRUCTIONAL STEPS

The listing of the operations, the information topics, and the making of a chart for an occupation or block of an occupation are important steps in making an analysis for instructional purposes. The materials covered so far are exceedingly useful to the experienced as well as to the beginning teacher. However, there remains another important step which is necessary to complete the analysis and which makes the analysis even more useful. Each operation and each information topic should be further outlined, or analyzed into steps. Merely listing the operations and the information topics does not give assurance that the teacher will fully cover each of them when teaching. The important steps that include the details of the exact manner of adjusting and manipulating tools in depicting, or shaping, or forming or assembling should be listed in their sequence, otherwise it is likely that

117

important points may be left out when teaching. This is just as likely to happen to an experienced teacher as to a beginner. Analyzing into steps gives the teacher material which is useful in making a practical daily lesson plan. For those who are interested in preparing instruction sheets or visual aids, this plan serves as a basic outline.

Operating Steps

In Chapter 5, information topics and certain points of auxiliary knowledge were explained. The latter belong naturally with and give meaning and existence to the operation. They are items of auxiliary knowledge. They consist of points relating to the *how* or *why*, or a safety precaution, or a new term, and the like, that must be covered in the lesson. Brought in as points integrated with the doing steps, they give meaning to the operation. If they are picked out and listed separately and scattered around on a card as in Figure 16, or as discussed on pages 69 and 70 in Chapter 5, their use in the teaching of an operation is practically impossible. In such a plan, the parts that make up the operations are scattered and must be brought together again in proper order when the lesson is taught. When such breakdowns are made, the purpose of analysis is ignored, or the maker is too inexperienced to understand that the analysis is for use of the teacher and not for display purposes.

Importance of Operating Steps

The integrated items of auxiliary knowledge must be taught by the shop teacher. They are sometimes thought, mistakenly, to be related topics and assumed, therefore, to be taught in separate lessons by the shop teacher or by the related subjects teacher. Certainly it would be unwise for another teacher to teach the *how* and *why* of an operation leaving the bare doing of it to the shop teacher. If points of safety were involved, it would be dangerous to leave them for others to teach. If, at a certain point, danger may be present to the learner, right then and there is the time to warn him. He must be warned before and not after it happens. He must be shown on the spot where it may happen and not at a remote time and place. Only general problems of

INFORMATION ANALYSIS

TYPE JOB __Cutting Tenons (Woodworking__ UNIT __3__ JOB NO. __4__

AUXILIARY KNOWLEDGE			TECHNICAL AND RELATED	
TRADE TERMS	TOOLS & EQUIPMENT	MATERIALS	MATHEMATICS	DRAWING
Table Fence Tenon Guide Grain	Power saw Pencil Ruler	Stock cut to size and marked for tenon	Use relay to 1/64 in.	Able to read plan
SOCIAL AND ECONOMIC INF.	HISTORY	SAFETY AND HYGIENE		SCIENCE
Pay by week or month Noisy Dusty inside		Keep to left of saw Hand on guide Use mat		Base of cutting hard and soft woods Size needed for strength

JOB ANALYSIS

TYPE JOB __Cutting Tenons (Woodworking)__ UNIT __3__ JOB NO. __4__

OPERATIONS	OPERATING POINTS	
	HUMAN	MECHANICAL

1. Read plan
2. Set up saw
3. Run stock through
 	
Operating Points (cont.)
5. Adjust height of dado
  a) Turn adjusting wheel
  b) Measure
  c) Try on scrap
  d) Readjust
	1. Take off blade
	  a) Loosen nut
	  b) Remove nut
	  c) Remove saw
	2. Put on dado head
	  a) Place wide on cutters
	  b) Place on washers
	  c) Screw on burr
	  d) Tighten burr
	3. Adjust fence
	  a) Loosen setscrew
	  b) Move fence
	  c) Tighten setscrew
	  d) Turn micrometer
	    adjustment
	  e) Place metal block
	    on end of fence
	4. Adjust slide guide
	  a) Right angles
	  b) Clean groove
		
		Fence moves

Fig. 16. *Job analysis card—obsolete and impractical.*

MAKING THE ANALYSIS—II 119

safety should be left to another teacher. Specific points in an operation at which danger may be present must be covered by the laboratory teacher.

Criteria for Teaching an Operation

One of the most important factors in teaching how to perform an operation is to present the safest methods of doing it. There are two other important factors: The operation must be performed (1) in the most economical way of using the material and (2) in the quickest way. There may be more than one way to perform an operation, but the safest and the quickest and the most economical way of using material should be presented. There is no excuse for assuming that occupational or industrial arts teaching can be efficiently accomplished by experimenting or by puttering. It is too dangerous and too costly. Good teachers are employed just for this reason. The instructional material therefore should be prepared in the most usable way.

Listing the Operating Steps

The further outlining of the operation into instructional steps, or operating steps, is not difficult, but it requires attention to the details of performing the operation. It is often necessary actually to perform the operation while making an analysis, to make certain that the major steps are covered and in proper sequence. The occupational expert usually has little difficulty with this step. Actual identification of the operation itself offers greater difficulty. Frequently, the operating steps are mistakenly called operations. This is especially possible when "uses" of tools or equipment are designated as operations. The uses of tools are covered one by one in the operating steps.

At the outset, one must list the first step in performing the operation, then the next step, and so on. Some steps may be *doing* steps, others may involve auxiliary knowledge. Some steps may involve some degree of each. In fact, it is difficult to separate *doing* and *knowing* steps entirely in an operation. A step may include an item of knowledge concerning the *how* of a movement, a new technical term, a safety precaution, a simple scientific fact concerning working qualities of stock, care of a tool in use, or use of a tool, and so on. It is usually an item that requires simple telling with a word or two rather than teaching. An operating step may involve any of these and more, but whatever the combination in a given operation, it takes all of them to make up the operation. The steps must be taught by the instructor in their sequence. It must be mentioned, however, that, as in building a house, certain things must be done first in getting started, but once under way there may be choice as to the next in order of the final steps. This is a matter for the judgment of the occupation expert. It is important, however, that all steps are included when making the analysis.

Again, be reminded that the analysis that you are making is for your use and not for the use of the student. It is your check list so you will be sure to cover every necessary point in teaching the student.

Attracting Attention to Safe Procedure

When a safety precaution is needed, it should be indicated in the step where the danger is likely to occur. The word CAUTION in capital letters or in italics should be used as the first word and followed by the desired precautionary remarks. It need not be numbered inasmuch as it is part of the step indicated. The following example is taken from the operation on page 123, *File Cylindrical Work in the Lathe.*

"3. Take long, slow strokes with little pressure.
Caution: File left-handed to avoid striking lathe dog."

The word CAUTION should be used as a red flag or warning that danger is impending or that a machine part or tool is likely to break. The latter may indirectly result in personal danger. Do not use the word *caution* for attracting attention to special information. The word NOTE should be used for this purpose and used sparingly because every statement is important and only special information should be specially identified.

Listing Steps in Advanced Operations

In listing steps for an advanced or cumulative operation—as for example "to square stock" in woodworking, Figure 7—it is not necessary to break the elementary operations into steps again. That was done when they were first listed. The elementary operation should only be mentioned, but the new principle or phase of the operation should be broken down into its steps.

Writing Each Step in Telegraphic Form

It is not necessary to write each step in the form of a complete sentence giving every detail. Each step need only be written in telegraphic form, or as a phrase or a word that will serve as a reminder to the person giving the lesson. Articles such as *the* and *a* can be omitted. The conjunction *and* can also be omitted and a comma substituted in its place. Outlining only, and not complete statements, is all that is needed. The instructor knows the detail and will present it, but he needs the briefly written reminders so that every step in the operation is presented.

List the Tools and Materials Needed

The tools and materials necessary to perform each operation while demonstrating to the learner should also be listed with the operating steps. This completes the outlining and provides ready information for preparing for the teaching of a lesson. The instructor needs only to examine the list to determine what tools and materials he should make available in order to demonstrate, and the operating steps he should cover in the lesson. New tools as well as new terms can thus be brought in at the place of application rather than in an unrelated abstract way as is frequently done when tools are named and shown in separate lessons, or when all the tools are listed and studied at one time. Listing all the tools of an occupation as a lesson in starting the course is not psychologically wise. A separate instruction sheet on tools is unnecessary. New tools and terms are best presented and best learned as they are used. A new tool or new term can be underlined in the operating steps so as to remind the teacher to explain it if necessary. This list of tools, materials, and operating steps makes a very satisfactory lesson plan for the teacher.

MACHINE SHOP
Knurl in the Lathe

TOOLS AND EQUIPMENT
1. Chuck, collet chuck, or driving-plate dog and centers
2. Tool post complete
3. *Knurling tool*
4. Wrenches
5. Chuck key

MATERIALS
Handle to knurl

OPERATING STEPS:
1. Select grade of *knurl* desired. Fine, medium, or coarse.
2. Set up knurling tool—at proper angle—must float.
3. Secure work.
4. Lubricate dead center.
5. Set slowest spindle speed.
6. Adjust lathe for coarse feed.
7. Start lathe.
8. Force knurling tool into work at right, about .015 or 1/64 of an inch.
9. Examine for uniform pattern of knurl.
10. Engage automatic feed.
11. Apply oil as tool travels across work.
12. Disengage feed when knurl is long enough—let cutter continue rolling to uniform depth.
13. Force knurling tool in .015 more.
14. Reverse direction of rotation of spindle, feed back.
15. Repeat until knurling is finished.

MACHINE SHOP
File Cylindrical Work in the Lathe

TOOLS AND EQUIPMENT
Mill file

MATERIALS
Cylindrical stock turned in lathe

OPERATING STEPS:
1. Select a mill file—clean and chalk it.
2. Double speed used for turning.
3. Take long, slow strokes with little pressure.
   Caution: File left-handed to avoid striking lathe dog.
4. Release pressure on return stroke—turns cutting edge.
5. Overlap with each succeeding stroke of file.

MAKING THE ANALYSIS—II   123

6. File to smooth surface—just enough to remove tool marks.
   Note: Very little filing needed. Too much filing causes uneven, inaccurate work.

WOODWORKING
Groove With a Circular Saw

TOOLS AND EQUIPMENT
1. Power saw
2. *Dado head*
3. Pencil
4. Rule

MATERIALS
Stock to be grooved

OPERATING STEPS:
1. Determine size of groove.
2. Set up saw.
3. Take off saw.
   a) Remove nut—do not force.
   b) Remove washers.
   c) Remove blade.
4. Put on dado head.
   a) Put on inside cutters.
   b) Put on proper spacers.
   c) Put on outside cutters.
   d) Put on washers.
   e) Screw on burr, tighten.
   f) Check for width outside to outside of blades.
5. Adjust throat space.
   a) Remove plate for saw opening.
   b) Replace with plate for dado head.
6. Adjust depth of cut.
   Caution: Saw must not be in motion when adjusting.
   a) Turn handwheel.
   b) Measure height with rule, tooth plumb, point to table.
7. Adjust fence.
   a) Release screw, move fence to desired position.
   b) Measure distance from fence to head.
   c) Adjust with micrometer adjustment.
8. Feed stock through.
   Caution: Keep hand on fence, stand on mat—not in line with stock.
   a) Feed steadily—do not force.
   b) Keep stock flat on table just ahead of saw.

DRAFTING
Sketch Arcs and Circles

TOOLS AND EQUIPMENT
2H pencil

MATERIALS
Sketching paper

OPERATING STEPS:
1. Determine proportional size.
2. Locate center.
3. Sketch *h* and *v* center line.
4. Mark off radii on each line from center—by eye.
5. Sketch 45-deg. radial lines through center.
6. Mark off radii—step four.
7. Sketch quarter circle—full, round arc.
8. Sketch next quarter circle—so on.
9. Examine work.
10. True up—smooth, full.
11. Darken line.

DRUGSTORE SELLING
Wrap Breakable Merchandise

EQUIPMENT
Article to wrap

MATERIALS
1. Shredded paper, or excelsior
2. Twine
3. Carton

INSTRUCTIONAL STEPS:
1. Select box, larger than article.
2. Place protective material in bottom of box.
3. Place article.
4. Stuff p.m. around article.
   a) Pack snugly.
   b) Protect all corners.
5. Place layer p.m. over top.
6. Close box.
7. Tie twine around both ways.
8. Wrap in heavy paper.
9. Tie securely—twine, two strands.
10. Label.

MAKING THE ANALYSIS—II   125

Rewind Armature

EQUIPMENT
Armature stand, fiber horns

MATERIALS
Wire, insulation

INSTRUCTIONAL STEPS:

1. Insulate slots.
2. Mount armature in stand, commutator to left.
3. Place wire in slot one, leave end 5 in.
4. Wind wire in slots as per diagram.
5. Make loop at end of turn, 5 in.
6. Continue with each coil group until windings placed.
   a) Pound wires in slots parallel.
7. After last set wires placed, fold over insulate on paper.
8. Wedge in slot wedges.
9. Bind armature.

TELEVISION SERVICE
Install Antenna

EQUIPMENT
Service repair tools

MATERIALS
Antenna kit

INSTRUCTIONAL STEPS:

1. Assemble antenna.
2. Connect lead-in to antenna.
3. Determine location antenna.
4. Install.
5. Construct tower.
6. Install arrestor.
7. Ground mast and tower.
8. Match lead-in to set.
9. Orient antenna.
10. Check signal.
    a) Lead-in for opens or shorts.
    b) Lightning arrestor.
    c) Lead off, set.
11. Check, eliminate ghosts.

126 OCCUPATIONAL ANALYSIS

ACRYLIC PLASTIC
Thread With a Die

EQUIPMENT
1. Stock and dies
2. Vise

MATERIALS
Round stock

INSTRUCTIONAL STEPS:
1. Select die, size, gauge, thread, NC.
2. Place die in stock, fasten.
3. Place stock in vise, protect, cloth.
4. Turn die clockwise, slight pressure.
5. Continue thread.
    a) Lub, mild soap solution.
    b) Die stock perpendicular to stock.
    c) Back every few turns.
6. Remove die counterclockwise.
7. Test thread in tapped hole.
8. Rethread if needed.
    a) Repeat above steps.

CLOTHING CONSTRUCTION
Attach Waist Band by Machine

EQUIPMENT
1. Machine   5. Thimble
2. Scissors   6. Pins
3. Thread   7. Iron
4. Needle   8. Ironing board

MATERIALS
1. Garment requiring band
2. Finished band

INSTRUCTIONAL STEPS:
1. Place wrong-side garment, right-side band together, centers matching.
2. Pin ends of band to ends of skirt, one side of band free.
3. Pin band in place, distribute gathers evenly.
4. Baste, stitch band in place.
5. Turn under raw edge, free side of band.
6. Pin band in position, just covering first stitching.
7. Stitch close to edge.

MAKING THE ANALYSIS—II   127

ELECTRIC ARC WELDING
Strike an Arc

EQUIPMENT
1. Hood
2. Chipping goggles
3. Leather apron
4. Gloves
5. Arc welder

MATERIALS
1. Scrap metal, ¼ by 4 by 6 in.
2. Electrodes

INSTRUCTIONAL STEPS:
1. Prepare stock.
2. Select electrode, size, thickness, position.
3. Set up equipment, approximate setting.
4. Lay plate on table, connect ground cable.
5. Place electrode in holder.
6. Adjust helmet, face, eyes.
7. Start machine.
8. Strike arc.
   Caution: Be sure your eyes and others in area are protected from rays before you strike arc.
   a) Movement, as striking a match.
   b) Draw electrode away from plate as arc forms.
   c) Draw electrode no more than ¼ in. away from plate, arc will break.
   d) When arc formed, adjust speed of travel suit conditions of weld.

INDUSTRIAL ELECTRONICS
Test a D.C. Generator

EQUIPMENT
1. Generator test stand, 0–10-volt d.c. voltmeter
2. 0–15-amp. ammeter

MATERIALS
Six-volt, 40-amp. automotive generator

INSTRUCTIONAL STEPS:
1. Test generator voltage.
   a) Mount generator in stand.
   b) Connect voltmeter across generator output.
   c) Operate generator minimum r.p.m.
   d) Record voltage output, increase r.p.m., increments 100 until maximum r.p.m. reached.
   e) Make voltage speed graph.
2. Load test generator.
   a) Operate generator at normal r.p.m.

128 OCCUPATIONAL ANALYSIS

b) Add load increments 5 amps to maximum.

c) Read, record voltage, current values.

d) Make voltage-load graph.

3. Operation test.

a) Connect battery to generator.

b) Close switch, observe motorizing of generator.

AIRCRAFT ENGINE MECHANICS
Prepare Engine for Disassembly

EQUIPMENT

1. Set of wrenches
2. Side snippers
3. Thrust nut wrench

4. Spark-plug wrench
5. 6-in. screwdriver
6. Oil pails

MATERIALS

Aircraft engine on stand (R-2000)

INSTRUCTIONAL STEPS:

1. Turn stand so engine is in flight position.
2. Remove safety wire, palnuts, cotter keys.
3. Remove oil drain plugs.
4. Drain oil into containers.
5. Remove main oil screen.
6. Examine for metal chips—indicates structural failure.
7. Remove starter nuts.
8. Remove starter.
9. Loosen but do not remove starter jaw nuts.
10. Loosen thrust bearing nut.
11. Unfasten ignition wires at spark plugs.
12. Remove spark plugs, place in rack.
13. Turn engine stand so engine in vertical position.

PHYSICAL TESTING LABORATORY
Determine Density—Dry Method

EQUIPMENT

1. Chain-o-matic balances
2. Weights
3. Micrometers (metric)

MATERIALS

Specimens for determining density

INSTRUCTIONAL STEPS:

1. Identity specimen.
2. Degrease specimen.

a) May use acetone or alcohol—remove all traces.

3. Measure accurately all specimens, metric units.

MAKING THE ANALYSIS—II   129

MS	DEPARTMENT VOCATIONAL EDUCATION DETROIT PUBLIC SCHOOLS	**TRADE ANALYSIS** INSTRUCTIONAL UNIT

Lathe

OPERATION _____ To Knurl _____ No.___ 38

TOOLS AND EQUIPMENT	MATERIAL
1. Chuck, collet chuck, or driving of plate dog and centers 2. Tool post complete 3. Knurling tool 4. Wrenches 5. Chuck key	Handle to knurl

OPERATING STEPS

1. Select grade of knurl desired: Fine, medium, or coarse
2. Set up knurling tool — at proper angle — must float
3. Secure work
4. Lubricate dead center
5. Set slowest spindle speed
6. Adjust lathe for coarse feed
7. Start lathe
8. Force knurling tool into work at right, about .015 or 1/64 inch
9. Examine for uniform pattern of knurl
10. Engage automatic feed
11. Apply oil as tool travels across work
12. Disengage feed when knurl is long enough — let cutter continue rolling to uniform depth
13. Force in knurling tool .015 in. more
14. Reverse direction of rotation of spindle, feed back
15. Repeat until knurling is finished

Fig. 17. *Operation analysis card, a simple recommended form.*

4. Calculate volume, cubic centimeters or meters.
5. Calculate weight, grams or kilograms.
6. Calculate density, formula $D = \dfrac{W}{V}$.
7. Enter data on record form.

After the operating steps have been worked out, and the tools, equipment, and materials have been listed, they should be placed on cards. A good card size is 5 by 8 in. but a sheet $8\frac{1}{2}$ by 11 in. is also satisfactory. The cards are easily used as the lesson outline prior to or during the demonstration. In Figure 17 is a sample card showing how the unit on knurling is presented. If an $8\frac{1}{2}$ by 11-in. sheet is used, the printed portion shown on the card in Figure 17 can be mimeographed.

130   OCCUPATIONAL ANALYSIS

It is desirable to make test questions while outlining the operating steps. These can be placed on the back of the card and used in the review lesson and in making an examination. This need not be thought of as part of the analysis procedure, though it is more readily done now than later.

This method of outlining an operation has much to commend it. It is simple and includes only what is necessary and what the instructor can really include in a lesson. It is in integrated form and each step is in sequence. The parts of the operation are not scattered as is shown in Figure 16, or as discussed on page 69.

As previously pointed out, it seems quite useless to break up an operation if the parts must be reunited sequentially in teaching a lesson. Moreover, when cards are thus made there is little encouragement to use them. Most of them are carefully laid away and ignored. The analysis should be immediately useful in teaching. Experience has shown that the form in Figure 17 has much practical value as a lesson outline and as an outline for those who write instruction sheets or prepare visual aids. It is simple, streamlined, and functional as compared to the form in Figure 16. Many things are listed in the latter that have little or no value in teaching a lesson. It results in confusion rather than order. Only what is necessary should be listed.

Lesson material such as that shown in Figure 16, the "technical and related" information and "social and economic" information, should be presented in other lessons and possibly by other than the shop teachers. If the facts are important, they should be fully outlined and placed on the cards. It is assumed, when they appear as in Figure 16, that they are to be included in the demonstration of the operation. There is enough to teach at one time in a lesson covering an operation without bringing in extraneous material. Only what is to be taught in the lesson should be listed.

Actually, the reference in Figure 16 to "Type Job" should read "Operation." "Job," as before mentioned, should refer to projects typical of the kind produced in the occupation, or to a repair assignment. "To Cut a Tenon" is an operation even if the analysis is based on production jobs in industry. The operations are the units to be taught in doing the job, and we are seeking the teaching units when making an analysis. It makes little difference whether "human" or "mechanical" operating points are identified and listed as such in separate places on a card in the breakdown of operations. Regardless of what they are, they must be taught anyway, and setting up classifications for them as in Figure 16 merely gives the beginning teacher another thing to complicate his work in analyzing the occupation. Each step is listed in its order of occurrence whether it is "human" or "mechanical." Let each step follow the other in the analysis and in the teaching of the lesson.

Information Outline

Information topics also should be outlined. The procedure is not unlike outlining in English composition. However, if a technical information topic is to be presented by demonstration, and when equipment and materials are involved, the outline would follow the form used in the breakdown of an operation as shown on page 123. Samples of several information topic outlines follow.

MACHINE SHOP
Milling-Machine Work
Technical Information
KINDS OF CUTTERS

1. Slab cutters
    a) Plain
    b) Spiral
    c) Diameter and lengths
2. Side cutters
    a) Plain
    b) Stagger-tooth
    c) Interlocking
    d) Half-side
3. Face mills
4. Angular cutters
    a) Single
    b) Double
5. Form cutters
    a) Convex
    b) Concave
    c) Gear cutters
    d) Special cutters

6. Saws
    a) Plain
    b) Chip clearance
    c) Special shapes for different metals
7. Key seat T slot, dovetail cutters
8. Fly cutters
9. End mills
    a) Two-lipped, straight, spiral
    b) Multiple-lipped, straight, spiral
    c) Straight shank—adapters
    d) Shell types

SHEET METAL
Technical Information

SOLDERS
1. Half-half—tin and lead
2. 60%—40%
    a) Stronger—free flowing
    b) Costly
3. Bar or wire form—solid or fluxed
4. Rosin core—electrical work and tin work
5. Acid core—use with copper, brass, iron, steel, silver
6. Special solders
    a) Copper, gold, pewter, silver
    b) Bismuth solder
        1) Lead, tin bismuth
        2) For soldering pewter—lower melting point
    c) Aluminum—Alumnaweld

DRUGSTORE SELLING
Technical Information
SAFETY PRECAUTIONS

INSTRUCTIONAL STEPS
1. Poison laws
    a) Sale of poisons
    b) Registration of sale and use
2. Narcotic laws
    a) Sale of narcotics
    b) Protection of drugs in store
    c) Prescription, renewals, etc.

3. Acids
   a) Storage
   b) Sale
   c) In prescriptions
4. Protection of physical safety of customers
   a) Keep floors clean, dry
   b) Keep sidewalks clean
   c) Keep watch of protruding objects

QUESTIONS

1. Why must all poisons be registered when sold?
2. Who is liable for injury to a customer in the store?
3. Why and when should renewals be illegal?

ELECTRIC WIRING
Technical Information

UNDERWRITERS' LABORATORIES

1. Who are Underwriters
   a) Testing organization established by National Board of Fire Under-writers
   b) Testing stations: Chicago, New York, San Francisco
2. Purpose of Underwriters
   a) Test samples of manufacturers' products
   b) Products must have minimum of safety, quality, utility
   c) Established standards
   d) Samples meeting requirements listed as: Listed by Underwriters' Laboratories, Inc.
   e) Underwriters' inspectors—to see that uniform quality is produced
3. Types
   a) Reexamination
      1) Not necessary to list large percentages
      2) Devices falling under this class: porcelain insulators, sockets, receptacles
   b) Labels to show list or approved
4. Labeling service
   a) Used where each piece of merchandise is individually labeled
   b) Types of labels: bracelet, doughnut
   c) Merchandise in this class: conduit, switches, lighting fixtures
5. How Underwriters are supported
   a) Fee for testing merchandise
   b) Manufacturer pays for more than cost of labels

134   OCCUPATIONAL ANALYSIS

THEORY OF ELECTRIC GENERATORS

1. Characteristics of generators
   a) Speed-voltage curve
      1) Shunt generator
      2) Compound generator
   b) Load-voltage curve
      1) Shunt generator
      2) Compound generator
2. Voltage control
   a) Manual
   b) Automatic
      1) Automotive, 6 volt
      2) Aircraft, 28 volt
      3) High voltage, 110 volt
3. Current control
   a) Field distortion, third brush
   b) Current regulators
   c) Reverse current relays

ELECTRIC ARC WELDING
Technical Information

TYPES OF ELECTRODES

1. Bare electrodes
   a) Solid metal
   b) No coating
   c) Brittle welds
   d) Subject to corrosion
   e) Straight polarity
   f) Low cost
2. Dusted electrodes
   a) With flux
   b) With less oxidation
   c) With high-tempered steels
3. Coated electrodes
   a) Dipped in liquid flux to secure gaseous blanket; protect molten metal from air
   b) Equipped with thread or wire reinforcements
   c) Produce deep penetrating welds
   d) Permit use of reverse or straight polarity
   e) Dipped liquid flux

1) Asbestos
2) Mica
3) Steatite
4) Titanium dioxide
5) Calcium carbonate
4. Special rods
   a) Nonferrous electrodes
      1) Copper
      2) Bronze
      3) Brass
      4) Aluminum
      5) Other
   b) Carbon electrodes
      1) Carbon arc
      2) Straight polarity

PHOTOGRAPHY
Technical Information

APERTURE AND SHUTTER SPEEDS
1. Aperture
   a) Relation to iris of eye
   b) Measured by F-stops
   c) Larger the F-stop number, smaller the aperture opening
   d) No effect on motion
2. Shutter
   a) Function of shutter
   b) Faster the shutter speed, less light reaches film
   c) Stops action, movement
3. Balance-shutter speed and aperture opening
   a) Factors affecting selection
      1) Movement of subject ups shutter speed
      2) Amount of light—low light, increase aperture opening
      3) Depth of focus
         (*a*) Close object—critical focusing
         (*b*) Larger the opening, less depth of field
      4) Brightness of object—dark or light
      5) Speed of film
      6) *Note:* Each F-stop gives half amount of light of step before it
4. Exposure meter
   a) Provides data for above

136   OCCUPATIONAL ANALYSIS

INDUSTRIAL ELECTRONICS AND INSTRUMENTATION
Technical Information

IRON-CONSTANTAN THERMOCOUPLE

EQUIPMENT	MATERIALS
1. Iron-Constantan Number 8 gauge Thermocouple	1. Thermocouple
2. IC Number 14 gauge Thermocouple	2. Head
	3. Milliammeter
	4. Matches for demonstration

INSTRUCTIONAL STEPS:

1. Thermocouples are widely used in industrial installations
2. Twist together at ends one piece of iron wire and one piece of constantan wire, two turns
   a) Make firm joints; take care that no strain or cracking of wire occurs
3. Attach free ends to milliammeter
   a) Mark each wire with spot of color for identification
4. Light match; hold flame to twisted joint—hot junction of circuit
5. Observe current flow—ammeter movement
6. Explain thermally-induced emf
   a) Produced almost directly proportional to temperature difference between hot-cold junction—Seebeck Effect
7. Explain heat absorption or liberation
   a) Current flowing through junction of two metals—Peltier Effect
   b) Heat liberated or absorbed proportional to quantity of electricity crossing junction
8. Explain Thomson Effect

MACHINE SHOP
General Information

HISTORY OF DRILLING

1. Crude drilling devices in use among prehistoric and primitive people
   a) Stone and shell points on wooden shaft
   b) Bow drill of American Indian
2. Civil War brought need for twist drill
   a) Drills made by hand filing prior to this time
   b) Flat drills or farmer drills
3. Twist-drill production in quantities dependent on developing of milling machine
4. Forging of flutes not quite general practice for large drills

MAKING THE ANALYSIS—II 137

General Information

MANUFACTURE OF IRON AND STEEL

1. Mining
   a) Where found
   b) How found
   c) How mined
2. Smelting
3. Blast furnace
4. Bessemer converter
5. Open-hearth steel
6. Electric furnace
7. Rolling mill

INDUSTRIAL ELECTRONICS
General Information

HISTORY OF ELECTRICITY

1. Beliefs of early experimenters
   a) Experiments
   b) Electrostatics
2. Men of history in study of electricity
   a) Ampere
   b) Argo
   c) Coulomb
   d) Edison
   e) Faraday
   f) Galvani
   g) Henry
   h) Lenz
   i) Oersted
   j) Ohm
   k) Peltier
   l) Plante
   m) Volta
3. Show "Thomas A. Edison" film

ELECTRIC ARC WELDING
General Information

COPPER AND ITS ALLOYS

1. Copper

a) Impurities
b) Effects of impurities
2. Brass
   a) Low brass
   b) Cartridge brass
3. Bronze
   a) Copper
   b) Tin
   c) Zinc
4. Gear bronze
5. Phosphor bronze
6. Leaded bronze
7. Aluminum bronze
8. Monel metal
9. Muntz metal
10. Copper-nickel alloys

PHOTOGRAPHY
General Information

SENDING PICTURES BY WIRE
1. Wirephoto (Associated Press, A.P.)
2. Telephoto (International News Service, I.N.S.)
3. Sending
   a) Photoprint attached to drum, emulsion side up
   b) Light beam focused on revolving drum
      1) Tool travels at it cuts piece turning in lathe
   c) Photoelectric cell picks up reflected light from photoprint
      1) Reflection varies according to light and dark
      2) Photoelectric cell converts light variation to current variation
4. Receiving
   a) Current received on telegraph wire makes similar light beam on receiving set pulsating in accordance with original variation
   b) Similar drum used, synchronized with speed of drum on sending set
      1) Sensitized film attached to receiving drum, emulsion side out
      2) Made lightproof by hood covering cylinder
   c) Light beam travels parallel cylinder exactly same speed as beam sending set
   d) Film developed and print made in normal manner

MAKING THE ANALYSIS—II   139

ELECTRIC WIRING
Guidance Information

APPRENTICE TRAINING
1. History—early days
2. Meaning of apprenticeship
3. Need for apprenticeship training
4. Group concerned
   a) Employers
   b) Apprentice
5. What the Voluntary Apprenticeship Law is
6. State Apprenticeship Council duties
7. Members of State Council represent employers and employees in various industries
8. Requisites of apprenticeship—age, agreements, employment, time required
9. Conditions of training
10. Completion of training
11. Related instruction—how provided, time required
12. Federal committee on apprenticeship—duties or functions

SHEET METAL
Guidance Information

IMPORTANCE OF SHEET METALWORK
1. Heating and ventilation
   a) Furnace pipes
   b) Stovepipes
   c) Hot- and cold-air pipes
   d) Smokestack
   e) Ventilator ducts, etc.
2. Air-conditioning
   a) Equipment
   b) Equipment enclosures
   c) Air ducts
3. Roofing work
   a) Metal roof
   b) Roof and chimney flashing
4. Gutter, downspout
   a) Fitting gutter
   b) Hanging gutter
5. Cornice work
   a) Moldings
   b) Trimmings

140 OCCUPATIONAL ANALYSIS

6. Metal ceilings—hanging
7. Finials

INDUSTRIAL ELECTRONICS
Guidance Information

ADVANCEMENT AND EDUCATION
1. Intelligence and health
2. Educational requirements
    a) Prior to training
    b) Courses
    c) Degrees
    d) Institutions for study
3. Salaries, work conditions
4. Specialties
    a) Power
    b) Distribution
    c) Communications
    d) Industrial electronics
5. Assignments
    a) Management
    b) Executive

ELECTRIC ARC WELDING
Guidance Information

STANDARD WELDING TESTS
1. Navy tests
    a) Navy Test No. 1—different positions, thickness to $\frac{3}{4}$ in.
    b) Navy Test No. 2—flat and vertical positions, unlimited thickness
    c) Navy Test No. 4—welding pipe
2. Boiler construction
3. Building construction
4. Construction petroleum high-pressure vessels
5. Gravity tanks, risers, towers
6. Heat, piping, air conditioning
7. Machinery construction
8. Pressure piping
9. Repairs on boilers, vessels
10. Storage oil tanks
11. Symbol test

FREE-LANCE PHOTOGRAPHY
1. Qualifications
    a) Courage
    b) Thorough knowledge photography
    c) Physical stamina
    d) Resourcefulness
    e) Tactfulness
2. Duties
    a) Takes pictures, sells them to publications
3. Earnings
    a) Based on sales, meager at start
4. Hours
    a) Must watch for picture at all times, day and night
5. Future
    a) After reputation established
    b) Writer, lecturer, picture editor, teacher, business, advertising, many more

The breaking down of operations and information topics is an outlining procedure. The information topics may be outlined on cards as are the operations, but it is a good idea to use cards of different color so they can be identified quickly. For example, blue could be used for operations and white for information topics. If a large number of cards may be needed, it would be desirable to print them. Much time is saved in making and in using the analysis, if printed forms are provided. In Figure 18 is shown a form that can be used for either technical, general, or guidance information.

If cards are not available, $8\frac{1}{2}$ by 11-in. sheets can be used. They are easily bound, if so desired, but not as convenient as the card in a teaching situation.

It is helpful to include references for information topics. This makes the method of instruction open to any plan of teaching. If related information is covered by reading, or presented by the related-subjects instructor or by the shop instructor, the references are useful.

Lathe
INFORMATION { General / Technical / Guidance — CALCULATIONS FOR TAPERS (Set-Over Method) ———— No. 106

1. Definition of taper
2. Kinds of tapers: (1) Jarno; (2) Morse; (3) Brown and Sharpe; (4) American
3. Calculations for cutting a taper
   A. By set-over method
      1. Change position of dead center
         a) Toward front of lathe
         b) Toward back of lathe
      2. Amount of taper determined <u>on the entire length of the piece between centers</u>
      3. The amount of set-over one-half the amount of taper reckoned on the diameter
      4. Formula:
         a) Work to be tapered entire length: $\dfrac{\text{L. D.} - \text{S. D.}}{2}$ = Amount of set-over

         b) Taper per foot specified on drawing:

         $$\frac{\text{T. L.}}{12} \text{ X } \frac{\text{Taper per foot}}{2}$$

         c) Taper per foot <u>not</u> specified on drawing:

         $$\frac{\text{T. L.}}{\text{T. P.}} \text{ X } \frac{1}{2} \text{ difference in diameters}$$

Reference: <u>How to Run a Lathe</u> by So. Bend Lathe Wks., pp. 59-64
<u>Mathematics for Machinists</u> by R. W. Burnham, pp. 97-101

Fig. 18. *Information analysis card.*

TEST QUESTIONS. It is desirable to make test questions while doing the outlining. As in the operation analysis, these questions can be placed on the back of each card and used in review lessons or in making tests. Examples of new-type test questions that appeared on the reverse side of the card shown in Figure 18 are presented. They cover the technical information for calculating tapers:

1. T. F. Taper is the difference in diameter for a unit of length of a conical piece of work.
2. T. F. Taper is usually stated by giving the *difference* in diameter for *one foot.*
3. T. F. The Morse Standard Taper is used chiefly on head-stock and tailstock spindles of lathes and on drilling machines.
4. ( ) The amount of taper is determined (1) on $\frac{1}{2}$ the length of the piece, (2) on the entire length of the piece, (3) on $\frac{1}{4}$ of the length of the piece, (4) on the radius of the piece, (5) on $\frac{1}{3}$ the length of the piece.

MAKING THE ANALYSIS—II   143

5. (   )   The (1) Jarno Taper, (2) Morse Standard Taper, (3) Brown and Sharpe, (4) American, (5) Sellers taper is used chiefly on headstock and tailstock spindles of lathes.
6. T. F.   For the turning and boring of tapers, the cutting edge of the tool should be set exactly at the center of the work.
7. There are . . . . kinds of turning and boring tapers.

Cards for the Teacher, Not the Learners

The analysis cards have little value to anyone but the teacher, and the teacher should make his own. Phrases and words that serve as cues to the teacher appear on the cards. The person who made them will best understand them. Complete information or instruction as needed by the learners may be in written form with pictures, reading assignments, or it may be presented orally by the teacher.

Summary

Each operation and each information topic should be further analyzed into steps. Merely listing the units of instruction does not assure complete coverage of a lesson by the instructor. It is necessary to list each important step in an instructional unit to be sure that there will be complete coverage. This is not difficult, but it requires attention to details of performance. These steps are frequently called operations, especially by persons untrained in analysis procedures. A step may include an item of knowledge concerning *how* of a movement, or *why*, a technical term, a safety precaution, a simple scientific fact concerning working qualities of stock, care of a tool, and so on. Some steps may involve knowledge, and some may involve performance; all together they make up the operation. These steps are listed in telegraphic form, and only those which are taught in a lesson should be listed. Complete statements are unnecessary inasmuch as the material is for use of the instructor who knows the detail and needs only the briefly written reminders. The tools and materials needed to perform and teach each operation should also be listed. This completes the outlining and provides information for preparing for the teaching of a lesson. It is a good idea to place the complete list of steps, tools, and materials on a card about 5 by 8 in. or on a sheet 8½ by 11 in. in size. This makes a practical lesson plan.

Information topics should be outlined on cards as are the operations; but if cards are used, it is a good plan to use a different color for the information cards so they can be easily identified. These are not instruction sheets. Instruction sheets would be prepared by writing up each step fully and providing necessary pictures for illustrative purposes.

ASSIGNMENTS AND DISCUSSION TOPICS

1. Tell all you know about an operation, its meaning, characteristics, application, and so on.
2. What is auxiliary knowledge? What is related information?
3. Name the kinds of information that you listed in the analysis of your occupation.
4. You should now have a list of instructional units for your occupation. Break down several operations into steps, list the tools, equipment, and material needed if you were to teach each operation. Have these checked by your instructors.
5. After you have had approval of your first attempts to break down the units, continue with breaking down the rest of the units of your occupation. Have your work checked from time to time.

FOR FURTHER READING

Allen, C. R., *The Instructor, the Man, and the Job* (Philadelphia: J. B. Lippincott Co., 1919), Chaps. 6–14.

Cushman, Frank, *Training Procedure* (New York: John Wiley and Sons, 1940), pp. 71–82.

Rose, Homer C., *Development and Supervision of Training Programs* (The American Technical Society: 1964), Chap. 4.

Selvidge, R. W., *How to Teach a Trade* (Peoria: C. A. Bennett Co., 1923), Chaps. 3–6.

Selvidge, R. W., and Fryklund, Verne C., *Principles of Trade and Industrial Teaching*, second edition (Peoria: Manual Arts Press, 1946), Chaps. 4–6.

Silvius, G. H., and Bohn, R. C., *Organized Course Materials*, (Bloomington, Ill.: McKnight and McKnight Publishing Co., 1961), Chap. 7.

8

Other Applications of Analysis

The occupational analysis technique is useful in discovering instructional elements in any area of world activity if what is to be learned is involved enough to require instruction. If there are fundamental elements, analysis is useful in discovering and listing them. Not only material things are created in the world by combining elements, but thoughts and ideas also are thus created. Whether an article or an idea is to be the outcome, there is problem solving; there is a human difficulty to overcome; there are elements of experience that must be combined to overcome that difficulty. Analysis can be used in systematizing instruction in any useful occupation even if it cannot be classified as technical.

Difference in Terms

The occupational analysis technique has been successfully used in analyzing distributive occupations, nursing, foods, clothing, police work, fire fighting, swimming, and many more. However, the terms used in production work to identify elements are not always applicable in other areas where material things, objects, are not created. For example, the term *operation*, which represents a unit of instruction that involves depicting, shaping, or forming of materials or assembling of parts, would not be a good term in analyzing distributive occupations. Yet, there are essential elements in selling that the salesman should know and be able to do. The selling of an article to a customer is a problem-solving venture in which fundamental elements are involved.

A few of these elements, taken from a list of instructional units for grocery selling, are:

DOING	KNOWING
Determine location of stock	Child-labor laws
Determine sizes of merchandise containers	Kinds and characteristics of merchandise
Check seasonable merchandise	Deriving selling prices
Pack merchandise containers	Cleaning compounds and solutions
Weigh on computing scale	U. S. postal rates and regulations
Package bulk goods	Customer buying motives
Sell by telephone	Store precaution measures
Handle complaints	General retailing policies
Make change	Local retail regulations
Make a charge sale	

In nursing, too, there are fundamental elements that represent things to do and things to know, but to call the *doing* elements operations would be quite out of place. A sample list of nursing units follows:

DOING	KNOWING
Open a bed for a patient	Poisons and antidotes
Make an occupied bed	Local infections
Change gown for patient	Bandages and binders
Adjust pillows	Senility
Lift patient and replace pillows	Thermometers

or back rest
Prepare for a doctor's
  examination
Take a patient's pulse
Give a bed bath
Take a patient's temperature

Clinical recording
Fractures
Convalescence
Dietary needs and methods of
  feeding
Accidents and emergencies
Communicable diseases

In police work, there are fundamental elements involved in performing the various duties but the terms used to designate elements in technical education would be doubtful in this work also.

DOING

Search a suspect
Apprehend a suspect
Transport a prisoner
Stop a car
Handcuff a prisoner
Follow suspicious person
Investigate a suspect
Examine windows and doors
Investigate a burglary
Make out reports

KNOWING

Laws of arrest
Getting along with people
Knowledge of the people on the
  beat
Court procedure
What to watch
Location of call boxes,
  telephones, signal lights on the
  beat
Building arrangements, streets,
  alleys on the beat
Location of safes and vaults on
  the beat
Kinds of reports

The following are additional samplings from analyses of other activities which show that certain elements must be identified for teaching purposes. They are *instructional units*. Some things must be done and some things must be known. They are elements which in various combinations brought about by hand and head overcome human difficulties or result in a human accomplishment.

FOOD PREPARATION

DOING

Weigh meat
Care for meat before cooking
Prepare cream soups

KNOWING

Classification of flour mixtures
Identification and uses of meat
  cuts

Prepare vegetable soup
Prepare pans for baking
Organize baking materials
Mix quick doughs
Care for baked products

Judging quality in meat
Weights and measures of
common ingredients
Causes of failures in baked
products
Factors affecting loss in vegetable
cookery
Evaluating recipes
Choosing baking powder

COSMETOLOGY

DOING

Adjust chair cloth
Dry hair after shampoo
Apply bleach
Apply astringent
Manipulate scalp for shampoo
Steam with towels
Loosen dandruff
Brush hair
Remove packs

KNOWING

Sanitary measures and controls
Elements and compounds
Normal skin and appendages
Kinds and purposes of various
shampoos
Skin diseases
Antiseptics
Sterilizing equipment
Kinds and functions of packs

CLOTHING

DOING

Select pattern
Check for size
Lay pattern on material
Cut garment pieces
Attach facings
Thread the machine
Sew a plain seam
Sew a French seam
Alter a pattern
Clip when fitting
Ease in fullness

KNOWING

Choice of hem finishes in relation
to fabrics
Causes of common machine
troubles
Names of materials from each
fiber
Causes of fitting problems
Makes of available patterns
Kinds of and uses of thread
Identification of quality materials
Sizes and uses of needles
Pattern reading
Modern sewing-machine
functions
Criteria for well-fitted garment

Music—Trombone

DOING	KNOWING
Hold the instrument	Reading music
Care for the instrument	Musical terms
Produce a tone	Harmonic series
Play diatonic scale	Half and whole steps
Move the slide	Tone quality
Tune the instrument	Mechanics of instrument
Articulate tones	Chromatic scale
March with the instrument	

Amateur Photography

DOING	KNOWING
Care for camera	Selecting film
Load roll film in camera	Planning pictures
Hold camera and shade lens	Selecting backgrounds
Center picture and release shutter	Selecting filters
Remove roll film from camera	Estimating distances
Load cut film in camera	Selecting shutter speeds
Remove cut film from camera	Determining "stop" opening
Adjust camera	Relation of light, film, shutter, "stop"
Assemble tripod and mount camera	Hints about the light meter
Assemble and adjust floodlights	Selecting lenses
Assemble and adjust flash gun	

Golf

DOING	KNOWING
Grip club	Power distance of clubs
Address ball—closed stance	Rules of play
Address ball—open stance	Judging distance
Make full swing	Judging quality equipment
Loft ball	Golf etiquette
Put backspin on ball	

Mechanical Optics

DOING	KNOWING
Write up	Reading prescriptions
True a lap	Indices of refraction
Rough up	Trade terms
Chill off	Dioptic system
Neutralize	Properties of abrasives
Decenter	Heat and glass

OTHER APPLICATIONS OF ANALYSIS 151

Rock a cylinder
Knock off buttons

Reading calipers

JEWELRY

DOING	KNOWING
Transfer a design	Design in jewelry
Solder	Stone settings
Anneal metal	Polishing compounds
Form bezel	Abrasives
Set stones	Alloys in jewelry
Model metal	Karat and weights
Chase metal	Chemical coloring of metals
Break stone	Enamels on metal
Saw or split stone	

SWIMMING

DOING	KNOWING
Hold breath	Water safety
Open eyes under water	Swimming tests
Combine stroke on front	Red Cross
Do front header	Resuscitation
Do flutter kick	Fancy diving
Stroke on side	Lifesaving

SILK-SCREEN PRINTING

DOING	KNOWING
Prepare paints	Design and color
Set guides	Printing surfaces
Clean screen	Sensitizing solutions
Cut film stencil	Silk-screen paints
Sensitize screen	Paper stocks
Make mimeo stencil	Stencils
Register multisheet poster	

PAPER HANGING

DOING	KNOWING
Prepare new surface	Estimating
Remove old paper	Colors
Tear paper	Kinds of papers
Hang short paper	Cleaning
Hang relief paper	Glue and sizing
Butt seams	Equipment
Make miter seam	Patterns

152   OCCUPATIONAL ANALYSIS

Units of Instruction

Inasmuch as the fundamental elements in any of these occupations are the things that must be taught to the learners, it would therefore seem satisfactory to call them *units of instruction.* This term applies equally well to both the informational and the manipulative elements. Persons in vocational education who find difficulty in accepting the term *operation* and its meaning in relation to the term *job,* but who accept the fundamental principle in all good instruction that there are elements that must be taught the learner, can take considerable satisfaction in the use of the term *unit of instruction* to refer to the *doing* elements or operations and to the *knowing* elements or information topics. The term *unit of instruction* serves well in any area when it refers to the elements that must be taught the learners. Whether an essential element involves doing or knowing, or both, it can be called an instructional unit.

Just as in mechanical work the operations are broken down into operating steps or points, as in Chapter 7, so in other areas, such as those just mentioned, the units should be broken down into steps or points and designated as instructional steps or instructional points. This applies to information topics as well as to manipulative or machine work.

Analysis in Plant Training

When systems analysis for industrial problem-solving reveals that there is weakness in production or distribution indicating limited abilities of personnel, something must be done about it and training is the answer. The problem remains until systematic training is successfully undertaken. Again, occupational analysis precedes instruction and the proved pattern presented in this book provides the specific training materials.

The principle that involves elements on the one hand and a problem on the other holds true in plant production except that a good many persons take part, instead of one, in producing an article, a part, or a subassembly.

Plants vary in their organization, materials, mechanics, products, and methods of production. However, there are custom occupations and repetitive work in most plants. The judgment of the person making the analysis will be necessary in determining which of the two charts, Figures 12 or 15, will be most practical to use. Custom occupations are represented in most plants in tool and die rooms, in patternmaking, and so on. Service occupations are represented in certain kinds of assembly and installation work. And, of course, in most plants repetitive work appears in greatest amount.

The assignments of persons who do very simple repetitive work and who do not require training aside from "breaking in" do not need analyzing for training purposes. The work of others who do complicated work, whether of repetitive or custom nature, needs analyzing. Inasmuch as only one article, part, or subassembly is produced in a department by a number of men, the chart in Figure 12 would not be necessary in analyzing plant training for repetitive workers. The chart in Figure 15, used in analyzing a service trade, is satisfactory for this purpose. Each machine can be considered as a block, and two columns, doing and knowing, can be arranged for each block; in most instances the knowing column is not as long as the doing column. The payroll job designation can be used for indicating the block, but in most situations in repetitive work the payroll job coincides with the machine, so either way of designating the block is satisfactory provided that it puts system into the training program.

Repetitive plant production involves all kinds of machines. Some of them are of the kind found in machine shops, and a good many of them are special. Each machine is used in doing one thing. Some are simple and some are complex. The production work of a department should be blocked; then the *doing* and *knowing* units for each block should be identified; then the units should be broken down into steps for teaching. Again, this assumes payroll jobs that are complicated enough to require considerable training of the learner in order to qualify. A specific formula for covering analysis for training purposes for all plants is practically impossible. The general principle of analysis applies, however, and the persons making the analysis should determine the needs after study of the plant under consideration.

Principle of Analysis Applied in All Areas

The general principle underlying the analysis procedure holds true in *all* areas of world activity where things are created and where human difficulties are overcome. There are essential elements on one hand and problems on the other. The essential elements must be combined into a necessary pattern to solve a given problem, as is done in mathematics. It is the teacher's duty to teach the elements in a practical way, the learner's duty to apply them in solving the problem. An article created in a shop, a machine serviced, a bill of goods sold in a store, an arrest made by an officer, caring for a newborn infant, and so on, are all human problems that involve application of elements in order to solve them, and they must be applied properly and at the appropriate time. The elements should be taught, but first they should be identified and listed. There must be an inventory that includes the fundamental elements and a goodly list of typical problems. The fundamental elements should be outlined.

Summary

This analysis technique is useful in discovering instructional elements in any area of work even though it may not be classified as a technical occupation, provided that the work is involved enough to require instruction. The terms used to designate the elements in one occupation are not always appropriate in designating elements in other areas of work. It is wise, therefore, to use the term *unit of instruction* when in doubt. It applies equally well to *doing* and *knowing* elements. The units always should be broken down into steps just as they are in analyzing an industrial occupation.

ASSIGNMENTS AND DISCUSSION TOPICS

1. Study your occupation and determine whether it is a single- or multi-block occupation. If it is a multi-block occupation, identify the blocks.
2. List the "manual" and "information" units and several typical work assignments in each block that resemble, or can be compared with, the elements of a problem in mathematics.
3. Place them on a chart as described in Chapters 6 or 7.
4. Break the units into instructional steps as explained in Chapter 8.

FOR FURTHER READING

Allen, C. R., *The Instructor, the Man and the Job* (Philadelphia: J. B. Lippincott Co., 1919).

Cushman, Frank, *Training Procedure* (New York: John Wiley and Sons, 1940).

Gaff, O. B., and Street, C. M., *Improving Competence in Educational Administration* (New York: Harper and Brothers, 1956), Chap. 2.

Prosser, C. A., and Quigley, T. H., *Vocational Education in a Democracy* (Chicago: American Technical Society, 1949).

Rose, H. C., *Development and Supervision of Training Programs* (Chicago: American Technical Society, 1964).

Selvidge, R. W., *How to Teach a Trade* (Peoria: C. A. Bennett Co., 1923), Chaps. 3–6.

Selvidge, R. W., and Fryklund, V. C., *Principles of Trade and Industrial Teaching* (Peoria: C. A. Bennett Co., 1946), Chaps. 4–5.

Struck, F. T., *Creative Teaching* (New York: John Wiley and Sons, 1937), Chap. 8.

About Learning and Teaching

KNOWING THE LEARNERS

You will be teaching the instructional units that you have listed in the analysis. Inasmuch as you may not have opportunity at the outset to study the principles of human understanding and learning so necessary in teaching, this chapter is included to provide a few lessons in dealing with students in a satisfactory way at the very beginning of your teaching. Those who have had beginning psychology will recognize the following and be interested in its application in technical teaching. This chapter contains technical information for teachers.

A few of the techniques of teaching a lesson are also presented briefly in this chapter because they, too, have relation to the application of the foregoing in presenting a lesson. Later you will be studying in more detail, in other courses and in other books, the lessons provided in this chapter.

Many situations in teaching are dealt with by using good judgment. The first thing that a new teacher should be able to do is to project himself into the situations of his students. By putting himself in the places of his learners, and by dealing with them as he himself would like to be dealt with, he is likely to keep up good relations with his students. He is likely to maintain good learning conditions, which are best maintained when all is well in the relations between the teacher and the learners. If he understands and is courteous and considerate and knows well what he is teaching and teaches it well, it will seldom be necessary to assert authority.

We Are That Way

What is there about people that makes them want to be dealt with understandingly? It is because all people have one thing in common. While people differ in most human characteristics, they are quite alike in one important respect: all people have feelings. What we do from morning until night is affected in some way by feelings. Let us think about ourselves. Feelings make us aware of being alive; they make us aware of things about us. Pleasantness or unpleasantness accompanies everything we do. We live constantly in the presence of feelings. It is a natural human condition. Were it not for feelings life would be impossible.

We do many things because of the pleasant feelings associated with them. Feelings condition the values we place on things. We seek entertainment of various kinds because pleasantness is attached to it. We like to look at beautiful things because of the pleasant feelings that come to us. We avoid things, when we can, if we believe that unpleasant feelings will be associated with them. It is a human characteristic to avoid the unpleasant and to do the pleasant. We are all alike in this respect even though we may not always recognize it in our daily routines. Reflect a little and see if you cannot trace many of your decisions and actions to feelings. They serve as controls of action.

Success is accompanied by pleasantness, and failure is accompanied by unpleasantness. Normally, one will strive to succeed; he may endure temporary unpleasantness hoping that eventually, just around the corner, lies success and its accompanying satisfaction. Success is inspiring; because of success there comes the desire to do even better. Failure is depressing, and too many failures are likely to inhibit further effort. Continuous unpleasant feelings are wearing on an individual; they sap vitality and breed indifference. The individual is in his highest state of efficiency when he is in pleasant adjustment with his surroundings. He can then put forth his best efforts.

What does this mean in teaching? It means just this: all people have feelings and, therefore, the learners whom we teach have feelings too. We must put ourselves in the places of these learners and treat them in the same way that we ourselves would like to be treated. There must be courteous, friendly, considerate dealings with our students. Tolerance must be shown when mistakes are made. It is the way we ourselves want to be dealt with. It is the way, therefore, that we should deal with others. This applies in any walk of life where people must deal with each other, work together, or even play together.

Only under rare and exceptional conditions should there be any variations to this practice in teaching. It does not mean, however, that sugarcoating and mollycoddling should be followed. A businesslike, yet pleasant, attitude should be present at all times.

Effective Teaching

Inasmuch as pleasantness is associated with success, we must teach our lessons so well that the learners will clearly understand them and thereby increase their chances for success. Our lessons should be organized so they will proceed from the simple to the complex. The early lessons should be simple so that success can come early. Early success brings hope and inspiration; early failure brings disappointment. We must not have situations that are likely to lead to failure, especially in beginning lessons. This is one of the reasons for arranging a progressive order of jobs or problems in making an analysis. Complicated lessons, if placed first in our plan, are likely to be too difficult, thus increasing the chances of failure.

When an individual seeks to do something, achievement is pleasant for him; but if one seeks to do something, and if he does not get to do it, it is unpleasant for him. This applies to learning. A learner should have the desire to learn, and for him to be taught when he has such a desire is satisfying to him. But if he is forced to learn, it is annoying and learning is retarded or prevented. One of the most important problems for a teacher is to get the learners to want to learn—to get them interested. Feelings of unpleasantness and interest go together. When a learner is interested, he is ready to learn and teaching is rather easy. When a learner is not interested, teaching is difficult and almost futile. So when you teach, see that your attitude toward the class is such that feelings are taken into account in every way because the learners have feelings just as you have. Be courteous and friendly, yet businesslike; be sure you have the interest and attention of your students at heart; have your lessons planned well and present them well so as to assure achievement. It will be satisfying to you, too, to see your efforts bring results. Success will come to you when you see success come to the learners, and it will bring satisfactions too—pleasant feelings.

People tend to want to repeat pleasant experiences, and tend not to repeat but to avoid unpleasant experiences. This is natural with most people. Impending unpleasant experiences are not viewed with pleasant expectations; rather they would be avoided if possible. An unpleasant experience is not to be repeated unnecessarily. If a learner is dealt with in ways that are unpleasant and if these continue, the classroom will be repulsive to him. But if conditions in every way lead to success, there will be the desire to continue to try because of the pleasantness attached to success. There must be accomplishment, and when there is, interest and attention are assured. A good teacher keeps the class continuously anxious to achieve. Early success by the learners is the best assurance of continued effort and success.

Learning and Habit Forming

Habits are developed by repeating experience. If we repeat pleasant experiences we make habits of them, which is the best way to develop skill. Skills are habits. Of course, we can repeat unpleasant experiences; we can force repetition against an individual's desires; but if all teaching were attempted on such a basis the learners would work against it. They would want to avoid such learning experiences. We want repetition and we can be certain that it will lead to development of skill when satisfaction and success attend one's efforts.

Just doing a thing once is not enough. Learning units must be repeated if skill is to be developed. They must be repeated under practical conditions because practical conditions are meaningful. Meaningful things are more satisfying than abstract things and, therefore, are likely to be repeated readily. A sure way to develop skill is to provide opportunity for repetition of the thing in practical applications. It should not be done by force or under abstract conditions as in repeating meaningless exercises.

Inasmuch as learning is conditioned by feelings, success and good feelings usually go together. The more one is certain of success, the greater the desire to learn; the more there seems likelihood of failure, the less the desire to attempt to learn. Shop experiences that are attended with success and satisfaction tend to become fixed with the learner, and shop experiences accompanied by failure and dissatisfaction tend to fade from the learner.

Building Confidence

Unpleasant feelings and failure tend to prevent personal development and to destroy confidence. Confidence in one's ability is a major desirable outcome of training. Anything that will destroy confidence should certainly be avoided. Be careful not to criticize too much and too often. Rather, find ways to commend; build on success; one cannot build on failure. A good house cannot be built on a weak foundation. Feelings, pleasant and unpleasant, underlie learning situations, and in terms of your own experiences remember that emphasis on pleasant situations is more desirable in dealing with others.

There are extremes in unpleasant feelings that may interfere with successful teaching and learning. Nervousness, fear, anger, worry, melancholy, and disgust are examples of such extremes. They arouse the whole body and interfere with learning and the development of skills. They tend to block the forming of good judgments in important situations; they are often the cause of accidents. Not all disturbances are recognized outwardly in an individual because some of them are internal. It is not uncommon to have headaches, sinking feelings, loss of appetite, poor digestion, or loss of bodily control when the extremes of unpleasant feelings are present. There is limited possibility of developing skills, gaining knowledge, or building confidence under such conditions. There are differences in people in their responses to extreme feelings. Some react more than others, but it is a good idea to assume that all are alike in this respect—and that unpleasant feelings are generally detrimental.

Learners who have tendencies to extreme emotional upsets require tolerant and sympathetic attention. You may not know how emotional a given learner is or can become. Learners are emotional in degrees that teachers do not often recognize and, therefore, it is advisable to guard carefully against arousing the emotions. Avoid ridicule, humiliation, and sarcasm with all students. Instead, try to do things that will build confidence. Confidence is a favorable attitude. It will help to suppress extreme emotional conditions. Be calm and have poise; be tolerant and sympathetic; yet be firm.

TEACHING THE LESSON

Development of skill in teaching is positively related to the foregoing lessons in elementary psychology. It has been indicated that pleasant feelings belong to the very warp and woof of successful teaching and learning. Skillful presentation of a lesson, therefore, is conducive to ultimate good feelings. The success of a learner depends in considerable measure upon the success of the teacher in accurately presenting the lesson. And the success and good feelings of the learner go together.

There are certain principles that should guide the teacher in presenting a lesson. The first one already has been presented, that of understanding the learners. Next, the teacher should know what he is to teach and the learner should know what he is expected to learn. Third, the teacher should know how best to present the particular lesson; that is, he should know what method of presentation to use. Fourth, he must have a thorough knowledge of the various aids and devices that have proved helpful in teaching.

What to Teach

The thing to teach is the instructional unit. The instructional unit is an element of the occupation. The elements consist of operations and information topics. One instructional unit and no more should be taught at one time. The steps to be covered in a single lesson are outlined in the analysis of the occupation. For example, in a machine shop the operation "how to knurl," already presented, would be covered in one lesson and would include all the steps involved in knurling and no more.

If the occupation has been fully analyzed so that each operation and each information topic has been broken down as explained in Chapter 7, you will then have an outline of what to teach in step-by-step order. You will have a set of practical lesson plans. If you examine the chart, you will discover which operations to teach first. The frequently used and basic operations must be taught first, just as the basic operations in arithmetic must be taught before advanced ones can be mastered. The basic operations form part of the advanced operations, and so appear at the top of the chart and have been given the low numbers on the chart and on the cards.

To repeat an often made and often proved statement, it is not the seemingly easy operations that should be taught first. The *basic* and *frequently used* ones should be taught first whether they appear to be easy or difficult. Individuals differ in every human characteristic including ability to learn easily the elements of an occupation. What may be easy for one person may be difficult for another. Therefore, the question of difficulty as a control of the teaching order may be dismissed in favor of the frequency of use of a given operation.

Teaching Methods

This entire book might be devoted profitably to the important topic of teaching methods as applied to technical education. Space and time limitations in the study of analysis, however, make it necessary to restrict the suggestions on method to a few helpful paragraphs. There probably is not a best method of teaching. The objective, the teacher, the learner, the subject matter to be taught, the time limitations, and the equipment and supplies available are major factors in determining the best methods of teaching in a given situation. The prospective teacher cannot devote all of his early training to the study and mastery of problems of method, but a few of the common methods of teaching are presented here for discussion.

1. DEMONSTRATION. Essentially the demonstration is an objective method of presentation in which the teacher himself conducts the construction or operation before the class or individual student and explains what he is doing as he proceeds. Demonstrations are widely used in medicine, physical sciences, and mathematics, and are usually supplemented with blackboard work. When used in this way the demonstration is sometimes referred to as the lecture-demonstration. If a best or most popular method of teaching shopwork were to be cited, unquestionably the demonstration would be named. It is useful generally in teaching.

In giving a demonstration, care should be taken that everyone is ready to be shown, that there is ample room for the demonstrator and for the learners, that the learners can see, and that they are checked from time to time to see that they really understand what is being done. The teacher can judge the efficiency of his work by asking questions or by having a learner perform a given step in an operation as the demonstration proceeds.

Care should be taken to see that only one operation or one information topic is taught at one time. There must be time for the pupil to master one lesson before he is exposed to another. This holds true in any method or presentation. Instruction should be centered on one thing rather than being spread out over several things at one time. Occasionally the teacher is tempted, because of a question from a learner, to digress from the main topic of a lesson. If the question or problem is an important one, it should be kept for a future lesson. Stick close to the assignment under consideration. But do not be discourteous in any way. If the question is a good one which would take too much time to answer, say that it is good, and good enough to hold over for later and complete discussion.

2. WRITTEN INSTRUCTIONS. Instructions which can be presented orally can also be written. Written instructions take various forms and are more or less difficult to write. Published instruction sheets covering the important operations and information topics are available in practically all occupations. They are inexpensive. It is well to note, however, that laziness overtakes many learners when using instruction sheets. Instruction sheets cannot simply be passed out and used automatically. There must be instruction on how to use them. The preparation and use of instruction sheets are so important that extensive literature is available and teacher training courses devote considerable attention to the writing and use of instruction sheets.

3. OBSERVATION. This is largely a procedure which involves watching others while they work at production. Oral explanation is not possible as in the demonstration given by the teacher. However, guidance is frequently provided by someone who points out the difficulties and niceties of procedure as the other person works. It is sometimes necessary to use this procedure in very large classes and under production conditions.

4. DISCUSSION. Discussion between teacher and learners and among learners is a helpful way of getting a lesson taught, but it needs careful teacher direction and control. Discussion is not highly useful in teaching how to perform mechanical operations, except as a means of clarifying points in the methods of experienced workmen.

5. RECITATION. Lessons for study may be assigned and the learners required to recite in question-and-answer form. This method is used effectively in teaching information topics to younger learners. It is not unlike the once popular grade school recitation method. Adults prefer general discussion to recitation.

6. LECTURE. The lecture method of teaching utilizes formally prepared oral discourses to which the student group listens. It is seldom used in technical teaching, because it is not effective in teaching production skills.

7. CONFERENCE METHOD. The conference method involves group discussion in situations when some of the members of a class presumably know more about a given problem than the teacher. The teacher then is essentially a leader and his duty is largely to keep the discussion within bounds and to emphasize or record the points brought out. The conference is suitable in new areas of instruction where methods are to be developed and in which there is practically no literature on the subject. Leaders are brought together to pool their knowledge. Experience has shown that the conference method has limits in teaching shop skills.

Teaching Aids and Devices

There is always need for aids and devices that will help in getting a learner to understand fully what is taught. Common, helpful aids and devices are textbooks, instruction sheets, pictures, drawings, sketches, models, patterns, charts, diagrams, reports, blackboards, motion pictures, still pictures, and so on. Shop teachers should ever be alert to developing and using teaching aids and devices. Not only are they helpful in the usual teaching procedures, but they provide variety and interest, and help to break the monotony of demonstrations and shop practice. Learning takes place in many ways, and the greater the versatility of the teacher in presenting lessons, the greater the certainty that he will reach all learners under all learning conditions. Readiness on the part of the teacher to use teaching aids and devices increases his skill as a teacher. Special teacher-training courses which especially deal with the making and use of aids and devices are available.

Steps in Teaching a Lesson

For many years four major steps in teaching a lesson have been used in education. They are known as the Herbartian steps. It is generally agreed that they are little more than theoretical steps but that they have value in analyzing a given teaching and learning situation. These steps are (1) preparation, (2) presentation, (3) application, and (4) testing.

Preparation is getting the learner ready to learn. All that has been stated regarding understanding the learner applies to the preparation step, one of the most important steps in teaching. If a learner is not ready to learn and does not know what he is expected to learn, little good can come from the presentation of a lesson by the teacher. Essentially this means that the teacher has interested the student and has maintained his interest. A good teacher keeps the learners in constant readiness to learn by the way he teaches and manages. An experienced, good teacher has made his control of the preparation step a teaching habit which needs little of his direct attention.

Presentation means teaching the lesson. Readiness on the part of the teacher to employ any one of the methods already mentioned and his versatility in bringing into effective use any of the many aids and devices are assurance that the lesson will be taught effectively, provided, of course, that the learners are ready to learn. An efficient teacher can readily shift his methods and devices to meet a given teaching situation. Yet, there seems to be no formula for good teaching that all teachers can use. Experience is necessary to develop ready ability in teaching just as experience is necessary to know how to cope with the many situations that arise in the practice of an occupation. Again, the nature of the instructional unit, the learners, the equipment the teacher's confidence, the place, and even the time of day are factors that condition the presentation of a lesson.

Application naturally follows presentation. The learner must promptly apply what he has been taught. Unless a lesson has been applied, there is little assurance of learning. We learn by responding and by doing what we have been taught and not by looking on passively. If an operation has been demonstrated, it should be applied immediately in a practical situation. If a mathematical procedure or other form of information has been taught, it, too, should be applied. The learner should be able to use what he has learned, and he should develop confidence in doing it.

The teacher should follow up the learner during application to see that he really understands a process or an operation and applies it properly. He must allow the student time, however, to attempt to apply what has been taught. He must not be too quick to assume that help is needed; there must be time to try. The help given must be limited to clarifying details which were not understood or learned or which are not applied properly. There may be need for repetition of all or parts of the presentation step.

Testing follows application. The learner should be able to use what he has learned without teacher guidance. There are different ways to test. Formal examinations can be given; the learner can be watched on the job; there can be recitations and discussions to bring out the learner's mastery of a situation. It is important for the teacher to be sure that the learner has learned and can apply what has been taught him.

Teaching by an experienced, efficient teacher is not necessarily a routine procedure of following the teaching steps just described in rigid serial order. Once teaching and learning are under way in a particular class, it cannot be said that a procedure following this sequence of steps prevails even under the best of teaching conditions. Preparation is a constant process affected by the attitude and application of the efficient teacher. There is an atmosphere of readiness in a well-taught and well-managed class. And so, presentation, application, and testing are continuous, not one necessarily preceding another, but each filling a need as that need appears. Perhaps only the first lessons of a beginning teacher hold to the sequence of teaching steps; then, as he masters teaching, any one of the steps may appear without concern about sequence. The teaching steps become habits that function automatically as need arises just as do the habits of the skilled worker.

Asking Questions

Asking questions and answering them, as put by the teacher to the learner and by the learner to the teacher, is rather a continuous process and necessary in technical teaching. The principles followed in understanding the learners should be present in the teacher's action. Courtesy, patience, and sympathetic understanding should prevail in putting and answering questions. There is no excuse for intolerance, sarcasm, or efforts to "show off" when questions are asked or answered. Again, remember, good feeling must prevail if good learning conditions are desired. There are a few points for the teacher to follow in asking questions:

1. State the question clearly. Questions in shopwork are usually related to the *why* and *how* of a problem.

2. All questions should be answerable. It is unwise to ask questions merely to bring out a learner's ignorance. However, it is not out of place to ask a question of an inattentive person to get his attention.

3. Ask the questions of the class as a whole. After a pause,

single out an individual for the answer. This keeps the group alert. Learners tend to relax if they know they will not be called on.

4. Do not permit group answers.

5. Every question should presuppose a previous experience that will enable the learner to answer.

6. Encourage complete and clearly enunciated answers.

7. Do not permit a few persons to answer all the questions. Hold all the class accountable by permitting each member to take part with reasonable frequency.

8. Questions that can be answered "yes" and "no" should be used sparingly.

Skillful questioning comes with experience. It is a necessary and important ability that forms part of the teaching skills of the good teacher. The question is a stimulator of learning and a means of holding learners to account for what they have been taught.

Class Management

Good management and good teaching methods go together. The teacher should organize the laboratory so that order and system prevail. He should enlist the help of the class in good housekeeping. In fact, one of the outcomes that should be expected from the learners in teaching is orderly procedure, good order, and respect for equipment and materials. Good management makes this possible.

The teacher should also be a business manager. He must know how to specify suitable materials and equipment and how to requisition them. He must keep account of tools and materials that are used. This cannot be learned quickly. Class and laboratory management is so important that classes are organized for training teachers in management as well as in teaching.

Habits of Work

Skill in performance and confidence in one's ability, both of which are highly necessary, have little practical value unless proper work habits have been developed. Learning how to earn means more than the development of essential skills; it includes also the development of earnest work habits. An employer cannot be expected to continue on the payroll persons who have not learned to utilize their time in an effective manner and whose attitudes are against the best interests of the employer and other employees. One of the major responsibilities of teachers is to manage the laboratories and teach the subject matter with a view to developing efficient workers.

There is danger when young workers, and old, enter industry with a feeling that something is owing them rather than that they have something to contribute for which they will be paid accordingly. Habits of loafing and too frequent rests should not be permitted in the school, and learners should discover the need of earnest application and speed. In the school laboratories conditions as similar as possible to those in industry should prevail, so that the learners will have little difficulty in adjusting themselves to payroll jobs upon the completion of their training. This training for industriousness can be and should be done in a tactful way. Some learners need not be told that they should work energetically and without loafing. Early in every course a few lessons should be given to make clear the expectations of industry in relation to work habits as well as to skills. To assure complete training, this much is due the learners.

Good learning habits and good work habits go together. Proper effort put into learning and progressive attainment will develop into ideas and attitudes of the kind that makes good workers. The returns are immediate in the learning situation; there is achievement, and the satisfaction of achievement is conducive to development of ideals and attitudes that lead to general personal attainment and development. These are components of the stuff that makes advancement possible on the job.

Text and Reference Books

Occupations are such because individuals have made discoveries, have learned new principles and techniques by experience, and have been thoughtful enough to put their findings in writing so that others may profit from them. Progress is due in large part to the fact that pamphlets, books, and periodicals which hold within their covers the instructions prepared by leaders in a given field have been made available to students and workers. Thus, vast stores of knowledge have been accumulated. In all education, an extensive literature has grown up and is available for students and workers who wish to make progress in their work.

The time is long past when the assumption that occupations and books do not belong together was accepted. The teacher who says that knowledge valuable for teaching occupations is not to be had in books is likely to be narrow and limited in his own work. He himself may be weak in his mastery of theory and practice. Or, if he is capable, it is quite certain that he has carefully kept out of view a well-worn set of good books. Considerable book material is available in every conceivable activity for every student or worker. The man is hard to find indeed who has progressed in his occupation without books. The teacher who really wants to make progress in his profession will accumulate a library of technical and professional books and be proud of the soiled pages attesting to the satisfactions gained by their use in moments of need.

Summary

A good teacher knows how to get along with the students. He is usually a good teacher because he understands human nature. He knows that the learners are possessed of certain human characteristics which make them what they are, and he knows that he, the teacher, has the same characteristics. Therefore, he knows that his dealings with the students should be in keeping with the manner in which he himself would want to be dealt with. He must be courteous, friendly, and considerate with his students. This holds true also of the teacher's dealings with all people, in or out of school. It is good psychology.

All people have feelings. They are influenced by their emotions from morning until night. People are attracted to and tend to repeat situations that have the suggestion of pleasant feelings attached to them, and they avoid and tend not to want to repeat situations that have the suggestion of unpleasant feelings attached to them. Success is associated with pleasantness, and failure is associated with unpleasantness. We should teach so well and organize subject matter in such a way as to insure early success. Early success helps in building morale for further effort.

Habits are developed by repeating experiences. Education is

habit building; a skill is a habit. Doing a thing only once is not enough; there must be repetition under favorable conditions in order that desire will be present. When there is desire, habits are more easily developed. Learning cannot take place readily under force or under abstract training conditions. Unpleasant feelings tend to destroy favorable personal development and confidence. Anything that will destroy confidence should be avoided; therefore the teacher should not criticize too quickly or too often. He should commend, if he can, before he offers criticism. Success is more easily built on success than on failure. Avoid ridicule, humiliation, and sarcasm; be tolerant and sympathetic, yet be firm.

Skill in teaching and understanding the learners go together. The teacher should know what he is to teach, and the learners should know what they are expected to learn. The teacher should know how best to present the lesson and, therefore, should be in ready command of various aids and devices that are known to be helpful. The thing to teach is the unit of instruction—the operation or the information topic. Each unit should be broken down so as to insure complete coverage in the lesson. The chart will be helpful in determining what to teach first. The basic and frequently used operations should be taught first, and these appear at the top of the chart. Difficulty, it was proved long ago, is not a factor in arranging an order of instruction.

There does not seem to be full agreement as to the best method of teaching because of the differences in teachers and learners. The demonstration, however, is conceded to be the most useful of teaching methods in all classes. Other teaching methods include written instruction, observation, discussion, recitation, lecture, and the conference. Common helpful aids and devices are textbooks, instruction sheets, pictures, drawings, sketches, models, patterns, charts, diagrams, reports, blackboards, motion pictures, slides, and so on. Learning takes place in many ways; the greater the versatility of a teacher in presenting lessons and in employing devices, the more it is likely that learning will be effective.

The Herbartian steps in teaching are (1) preparation, (2) presentation, (3) application, and (4) testing. These steps represent a sequence in teaching a formal lesson, but they should not be assumed as rigid patterns because, once teaching gets started, need determines which of the steps will function. These steps are descriptive of what happens as good teaching habits automatically come into use. They should be planned for by the beginning teacher, and practice should make them habitual.

The technique of questioning should be mastered by every teacher. The question stimulates learning and is a means of holding the learners to account for what has been taught. Good management and good teaching methods go together. A good teacher is also a good manager.

Good work habits should be developed along with production skills. Conditions in industry should prevail in the school shops so that the learners will have little difficulty in adjusting themselves to payroll jobs upon the completion of their training. Good learning habits and good work habits go together.

Each person who wants to make progress will accumulate a library and use it continuously in advancing himself. The person is hard to find who has made progress without the use of good books.

DISCUSSION TOPICS

1. Why do we do as we do?
2. What are the characteristics of a good teacher?
3. Make a list of things that a good teacher should do and another list of things he should not do.
4. What are feelings? Name some situations in which feelings controlled your action.
5. Make a list of the likely results if a teacher disregards feelings in his dealings with the learners.
6. Give the meaning of simplicity and complexity in relation to success in learning.
7. Tell how a demonstration should be presented.
8. Tell how a habit in correct shop performance is best developed.
9. What are the effects of extreme emotions on learning?
10. What are instructional units?
11. Would you ask questions of a class while you are demonstrating a lesson? Give reasons for your point of view.
12. What does "preparation" mean in the formal steps of teaching?
13. How should questions be asked?
14. Make a list of management duties.
15. Make a list of difficulties that may arise if management is weak.

16. What are you planning to do to encourage development of good work habits in the learners?

FOR FURTHER READING

Allen, C. R., *The Instructor, the Man, and the Job* (Philadelphia: J. B. Lippincott Co., 1919), Chaps. 23–28.

Bass, M. B., *Fifty Hints for Teachers of Vocational Subjects* (Chicago: American Technical Society, 1940).

Bonner, Hubert, *Psychology of Personality* (New York: Ronald Press Company, 1961), pp. 151–153, 305–307.

Ericson, E. E., and Seefeld, Kermit, *Teaching Problems in Industrial Arts* (Peoria: C. A. Bennett Co., 1960).

Jones, W. B., *Problems in Teaching Industrial Arts and Vocational Education* (Milwaukee: The Bruce Publishing Co., 1958).

Micheels, W. J., and Karnes, M. R., *Measuring Educational Achievement* (New York: McGraw-Hill Book Co., 1950).

Morgan, C. T., *Introduction to Psychology* (New York: McGraw-Hill Book Co.), Chap. 4.

Pankowski, Dallas, "A Guide for the Development of Motor Skills," *Industrial Arts and Vocational Education*, Vol. 54, No. 2, February, 1965, pp. 24–26.

Ray, W. S., *The Science of Psychology* (New York: The Macmillan Co., 1964), pp. 57–62.

Selvidge, R. W., *How to Teach a Trade* (Peoria: C. A. Bennett Co., 1923), Chaps. 8–10.

Selvidge, R. W., and Fryklund, V. C., *Principles of Trade and Industrial Teaching* (Peoria: C. A. Bennett Co., 1946), Chaps. 10–19.

Sorenson, Herbert, *Psychology of Education* (New York: McGraw-Hill Book Co., 1964).

Struck, F. T., *Creative Teaching* (New York: John Wiley and Sons, 1938).

Thorpe, L. D., and Cruze, W. W., *Developmental Psychology* (New York: Ronald Press Co., 1956), Chap. 8.

Course Development

Making an occupational analysis is not the same as preparing a course of study. It is the gathering of subject-matter materials for use in developing courses of study. The inventory procedure that was described in the earlier chapters provides instructional units from which the subject-matter content for more than one course of study can be selected. There may be enough in one analysis to provide content for several courses of study.

In this chapter the procedure for developing courses of study will be outlined, but it should be made clear that one cannot learn to make a course of study in less time than one can learn to make an analysis of an occupation. Special study and writing are required. A well-balanced teacher-education program usually includes instruction in the principles of course development. It is not intended here to give more than a summary of the usual procedure for making a course of study that will be helpful in your immediate plans for preparing to teach. It also shows the relation of the analysis to course development.

What Is a Course of Study?

A course of study is an organized body of material necessary for the teaching of a particular subject. It is distinguished from the *curriculum* by the fact that the latter includes all the courses of study offered over a long period of time and required to train for a vocation. Courses of study from several departments in a school may be included in a curriculum. In a school the curriculum of the electrical department would include all the shop courses, English, science, mathematics, and other offerings necessary in the training of electricians. The organized materials for a course in beginning electricity, however, is a course of study.

A course of study should have in it several important things. It is more than a mere list of units to be taught or a list of projects. It should be a guide for the teacher in performing all the work necessary to teach a class, and *it should be a relative rather than an absolute guide*. Individual differences in abilities of learners should always be taken into account, and therefore absolute rigidity should not be expected in carrying out the suggestions offered in a course of study. On the whole the course should be followed, but the teacher also should be ready to make modifications to meet individual needs, especially needs that point to progress in that activity.

A course of study should include the following main divisions: (1) a clear statement covering the grade level or placement of the students and their types and ages, the time, equipment, materials available, and any other information of value in orienting the problem; (2) a set of aims for the course; (3) the content of the course, consisting of a list of instructional units and suggested typical jobs selected from the analysis of the occupation; (4) suggested teaching and management procedures; (5) suggested testing or evaluating procedures; (6) resource materials, such as texts and references, requisition procedures, safety regulations of the school, information covering supplementary services such as clubs in which the students may take part, drawings of projects, sample instruction sheets, new ideas and designs, plans, a glossary, and any other materials supplementary to carrying out successfully the duties involved in teaching a given subject. These miscellaneous materials should be placed in the final section, usually called the Appendix.

A course of study can be brief or very detailed. However, the more resource materials it contains, the more useful it will be to the teacher. Course development, therefore, should not be too quickly done. Adequate time should be devoted to make it thorough. In a large city system, when there are many teachers of one subject, it is advisable to build and revise courses of study periodically through committees which thus divide the duties. Courses usually are flexible and subject to revision as need occurs; hence the expression *course development* rather than *course construction*. The course of study should be a guide to the teacher, not unlike handbooks used for technical purposes, with the exception that it is limited to a single subject. Perhaps a complete course of study should properly be called the teacher's handbook.

Matters of Orientation

Course development starts with determining what is to be done and the probable limitations of the course. At the outset, therefore, a statement must cover what the subject is for which the materials are to be used. Is the subject for occupational-training purposes; is it assumed to be for a semester or for a year; how much time per week and per day will be given to the subject; what equipment and materials are available; what is the location of the school; and what are the community characteristics? These topics should be carefully covered at the outset because, one way or other, they are factors which modify the subject matter, the method of teaching, and management. These factors vary in their extent of influence. For example, it would seem that the location of the school and the people served in one community would affect many things in the preparation of class materials, the method of dealing with the learners, management, and so on. Yet in another community the same factors may not be important. It is advisable, therefore, to begin the necessary groundwork for developing a course by considering all the variable factors and listing them before proceeding with the preparation of the course.

Determination of Aims

The next step in course making is selection or determination of aims. There must be aims in a course of study just as there must be aims in any worthwhile undertaking. There must be aims that can be realized by the learners and the teacher. Aims are for both learners and teachers, and the course of study is an outline of the means of attainment.

Aims should indicate what is to be accomplished. They should not be claims; they should indicate certain responsibilities of attainment. They, therefore, should have certain functions. *First,* they should indicate the end toward which instruction in the subject should move. They help the teacher to determine the proper direction and to keep instruction within bounds. *Second,* they should help the teacher to determine when the desired end of instruction in the subject is reached. *Third,* they should serve as a guide in determining what content shall be chosen, which, when accompanied by good instruction, will make the best contribution to the realization of the aims. Any content that would not contribute to the desired end should be rejected. It is difficult to know what content to accept or reject unless aims are definitely stated. *Fourth,* the aims of a subject should help to determine what methods of instruction should be employed in order to teach the content. Proper instructional emphasis in terms of desired ideals, attitudes, appreciations, and skills would be difficult without subject aims. *Fifth,* they should indicate the nature of the testing or appraisal procedures that should be employed in evaluating results. They should be of help in setting up objectives for constructing examinations and for evaluating results. Tests are important for determining when the aims have been attained.

Selection of Content

A natural next step is the selection of course content. Content should be selected from the analysis of the occupation or activity in question. Analysis can be undertaken at any time prior to or simultaneously with course-making. It serves as a check to assure thoroughness and completeness. The content should be expressed in terms of essential elements: (1) the related information, (2) the hand and machine skills, and (3) suitable individual or group projects, or work assignments, in which the fundamentals should be applied.

Teaching Methods

A logical next major step in making the course of study is the consideration of the teaching techniques and devices that will best contribute to the realization of the aims of the subject. The proposed teaching procedure should be stated in the course of study.

The attainment of desired results, through the attainment of aims, is limited in part by the method of teaching. In a technical school, or in senior high school, skills may be the desired results of instruction in certain learning units. In another school, or at lower grade levels, appreciation rather than skills may be among the desired results. Methods of teaching rather than the list of learning units would then control the emphasis.

It goes without saying that while the content may be well chosen, the aims may not be attained because of a misunderstanding of the desired results and failure in the methods of teaching. Moreover, the nature of the content of a course and its organization have much to do with the choosing of effective instructional procedures and devices.

A teacher's working knowledge of the principles of psychology will be helpful as a guide in method, in order that the best practices of instructional procedure may be followed. Among others, examples of such need appear in the problem of coping with individual differences in learning, and the problem of teacher-learner relations.

In large measure, any methods or combination of techniques of instruction that can be used in teaching technical work depend for their success upon good management. Good management makes possible the routine movements of the learners so that a maximum amount of liberty is permitted. It helps to create an atmosphere of active interest and industry. Any plans for teaching method, therefore, should also include plans for management.

Testing and Evaluating Results

One of the best ways of knowing that the aims of instruction have been reached, and that there has been proper emphasis for attaining desired results, is the use of tests.

Any tests used to evaluate results should be constructed according to the aims of the course. If the aims are conceived in terms of ideals, attitudes, appreciations, and skills, then the tests should measure these qualities according to the desired emphasis. However, it hardly seems necessary to measure manipulative skills beyond the appraisal made in the routine of the teacher's observations. Adequate judgment of performance can, for practical purposes, be determined by judgment of the teacher.

Evaluation of results does not assume formal testing only. Appraisal by informal evaluation procedures of shopwork and knowledge is exceedingly valuable. Frequent, informal written and oral questions of appraisal are desirable in addition to a formal plan of testing.

In technical work, as in other areas of education, there are direct and indirect results. The indirect results, or concomitants, are not readily measurable. The concomitants are the learning that takes place rather incidentally, such as the development of good work habits. These are considered by many teachers, even though hardly measurable, to be fully as important as is the direct learning specified by the aims and content. The teacher, his organization of content, and his methods influence the value of concomitant learning to a high degree.

The informational results are more easily measurable by paper tests than are manipulative skills. However, the possession of certain mental skills can also be measured by paper tests. Samples of typical types of test elements and plans for testing should appear in a course of study.

Texts and Reference Materials

It would seem necessary, in making a course of study, to include a list of texts and reference materials. Such a list, in a printed document, logically follows rather than precedes the presentation of the course, just as a bibliography follows the discourse in any scientific reporting. Therefore, books and materials used in the making of a course, and books and materials of value in teaching, should be listed separately in the Appendix. A course of study is exceedingly valuable to a teacher when it has a bibliography.

Supplementary Services and Materials

The appendix should include a list of materials such as sample tests, a bibliography, suggested plans of organization, laboratory layouts, lists of available supplies, equipment, directions for requisitioning supplies, safety regulations, lists of extracurricular organizations such as craft clubs, drawings of projects, suggested plans for grading and recording, sample instruction sheets, list of available visual aids, and a glossary.

New ideas should be continuously added—ideas that enrich the course and make it more valuable as a guide.

It may not seem necessary and desirable to include all of these matters in every course of study, but when they are included they should be there because of their usefulness to the full functioning of the course. It should be understood that many things seemingly outside the course of study itself have considerable influence on the direct and indirect learning of the students. Since supplementary materials do not readily fall into the sequence of presentation of a course of study, they are best included in the Appendix.

Summary

Making a course of study is not the same as analysis. A course of study is the organized body of material necessary for the teaching of a particular subject. It is distinguished from a curriculum because the latter includes all the subjects necessary to prepare for a vocation. The course of study should be a guide for the teacher in performing all the work necessary to teach a class properly. It should include (1) clear statements that should be of value in orienting the problem, (2) a set of course aims, (3) the course content, consisting of instructional units and suggested jobs selected from the analysis of the occupation or activity, (4) suggested teaching and management procedures, (5) suggested testing and evaluating procedures, and (6) miscellaneous suggestions and directions, such as text and reference materials, requisition procedures, safety regulations of the school, information covering supplementary services such as clubs, drawings of projects, sample instruction sheets, visual aids, a glossary, and any other materials that will be helpful to the teacher. All items of miscellaneous nature belong in the Appendix.

A course of study should be very detailed. The more it has in it that will be of help to the teacher, the more it is likely to be used. It takes time to build a good course of study. It is a good plan to have committees assigned to the task in the larger cities where several teachers offer the same subject. A course of study should be complete enough to be like a technical handbook in its usefulness to the teacher.

ASSIGNMENTS AND DISCUSSION TOPICS

1. What is a course of study? A curriculum?
2. Make a list of things of orientation nature that would need consideration in your school before working on a course of study.
3. What should be included in a course of study?
4. What is the importance of aims in a course of study? Should there be relationship between school aims and the course aims?
5. How can teaching methods be a cause of success or failure in using the course of study?
6. How can clubs and other extracurricular activities be of value to class instruction? Why should clubs and social services be considered in preparing a course of study?
7. Give a list of things that you believe should be included in the Appendix.

FOR FURTHER READING

Dewey, John, *Experience and Education* (New York: The Macmillan Co., 1938).

Ericson, E. E., and Seefeld, Kermit, *Teaching the Industrial Arts* (Peoria: C. A. Bennett Co., 1960), pp. 15–162.

Friese, John F., *Course Making in Industrial Education* (Peoria: C. A. Bennett Co., 1958).

Fryklund, Verne C., and Bedell, Earl L., "Course of Study Construction in Industrial Education," *Industrial Arts and Vocational Education*, Vol. 28, Nos. 7 and 8, September–October, 1939, pp. 261–263, 311–314.

Giachino, J. W., and Gallington, R. O., *Course Construction in Industrial Arts and Vocational Education* (Chicago: American Technical Society, 1961).

Haws, R. W., and Schaefer, C. J., *Manufacturing in the School Shop* (Chicago: American Technical Society, 1960).

Hopkins, L. T., *Curriculum Principles and Practices* (Chicago: B. H. Sanborn and Co., 1930).

Jones, W. B., *Problems in Teaching Industrial Arts and Vocational Education* (Milwaukee: The Bruce Publishing Co., 1958).

Krug, A. K., *Curriculum Planning* (New York: Harper and Brothers, 1957).

Rose, Homer C., *Development and Supervision of Training Programs* (Chicago: American Technical Society, 1964), Chap. 9.

Selvidge, R. W., and Fryklund, V. C., *Principles of Trade and Industrial Teaching*, 2 ed. (Peoria: Manual Arts Press, 1946).

Silvius, G. H., and Bohn, R. C., *Organizing Course Materials* (Bloomington, Ill.: McKnight and McKnight Publishing Co.), Chaps. 1, 3.

Struck, F. T., *Creative Teaching* (New York: John Wiley and Sons, 1938).

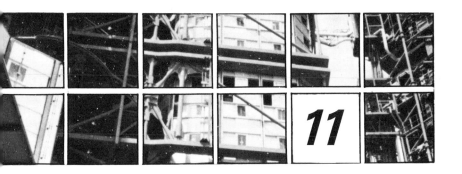

Problem-Solving

Every subject area in the schools should include in its offerings instruction that will subsequently enable its students to think purposefully and to reason through problems of its special kind. There should be problem-solving experiences peculiar to the field under study, whether it be mathematics, science, fine arts, music, business, shop, or something else. While everyone may not gain high proficiency in effective thinking procedures or in problem-solving, everyone should be given an opportunity to develop such abilities as early as possible. Attainment of success in the world of work is closely associated with purposeful and effective thinking. In vocational-technical and industrial arts teaching, problem-solving has its roots in analysis.

There should be organized instruction in problem-solving so there can be review and evaluation of the procedure. Care should be taken that "problem-solving" does not become an excuse to cover up lack of personal skill on the part of the teacher, or that shop keeping is not substituted for teaching. Skills and problem-solving should be taught according to a systematic plan. A practical and much used plan is presented in this chapter.

Teach How to Think

Teachers in the various technical areas share the responsibility of including as one of their major aims the task of teaching the learners how to think purposefully and effectively. In the technical areas there are problems in abundance; there is no end to the opportunities to guide youth in developing the initiative needed in solving typical problems. Unfortunately these opportunities often go unnoticed or unidentified. This is likely to occur if the teacher has not been instructed in the method of analysis and its relation to good teaching. He has difficulty in identifying instructional units in a given activity and therefore does not teach them. He does not distinguish the fundamentals to be taught from the problems to be solved. Shopwork thus becomes puttering or "busy work" because of misplaced emphasis related to purposeful thinking, since only a minimum of learning takes place through casual instruction. Thus, more had habits than good ones are formed.

Mathematics Sets the Pattern

In all subjects that involve creative work there are problems typical of the area. There are fundamentals which, in various combinations, are necessary to the solution of the problems. Judgments are formed by the problem-solver in combining these fundamentals so that the particular combination becomes the solution of the problem in question. There must be proved experience from which to draw because problem-solving cannot be done in a vacuum. Mathematics is a good illustration of this. In mathematics problem-solving is evident to everyone, whereas in other areas it is determined by special analysis and synthesis. In mathematics there are operations, which combine in patterns determined by the problem-solver, and which are necessary to the solution of a particular problem. These operations are quite *constant*. They have existed through the ages and will continue to exist. The problems, however, are *variables*, and they change as technology changes and as civilization advances.

There are problems today that were not evident years ago; and, no doubt, years hence there will be problems that are not foreseeable today. But the fundamentals, the elements necessary in the solution of problems, will remain quite the same through the ages. Today there are problems in aerospace design that are solved by the same mathematical operations, but in different combinations, that were necessary in the solution of problems that existed long before the space age. Machines and automation may expedite computation or mechanical performances, but the principles underlying problem-solving remain the same.

In occupations there are fundamentals, operations, and technical information topics that are *constant*. There are problems or variables that are solved through combinations of these operations and information topics. The problems, as stated in earlier chapters, are the projects or jobs of the kind typical of the activity. A combination of manipulative or machine operations and the necessary technical information brings about the solution of a particular problem, and results in the successful completion of a project with its attendant learning. The planning of a procedure and the subsequent production serve as vehicles for instruction in problem-solving in technical work, just as problems serve as vehicles for instruction in mathematics.

In all good teaching the instructor teaches the fundamentals necessary in the solution of problems. In such teaching typical problems are used in giving experiences in combining the fundamentals in necessary patterns. There is practice in solving problems by application of the combinations of operations and information topics that have been taught. New operations and information topics are taught continuously, which in combination with units previously taught, are applied by the learner in the solution of new problems as they appear.

Problem-Solving Not Inductive Teaching of Operations

Unfortunately, there are some advocates of problem-solving experiences in technical teaching who assume that inductive teaching of operations is the sole approach to development of problem-solving abilities. A few operations may be learned in that way, but trial and error is less applicable in teaching technical skills than it is in mathematics where there is no danger to a person or a machine. Trial and error in learning to perform manipulative or machine operations is in most cases very dangerous to the person, destructive of equipment, and wasteful of materials and time. Such an approach is a misconception of the meaning of problem-solving in technical teaching. Safety education cautions against methods that may lead to accidents. A major purpose of providing instruction in problem-solving techniques is to develop habits of purposeful thinking in all endeavors relating to technical laboratories.

Plan of Procedure the Point of Emphasis

At no time should the teacher tell the learner how to solve a particular problem. This would deprive him of opportunity to learn how to think effectively. The major achievement is not just the performing of manipulative or machine operations in the making of projects, with the instructor at hand to tell when and where the operations must be performed. When a given operation has been completed on a project, it should not be necessary for the teacher to tell the learner what should be done next. The teacher should not indicate each step or give the learner a list of tools and materials that will be needed in construction. Teaching conducted in such a manner would have little if any educational value. It would be *shop keeping* rather than *shop teaching*. It would be telling *what to think*, but it would not be teaching *how to think*.

The plan of procedure is the best means of teaching how to solve problems in shop instruction. It is the device used by the good teacher to determine how well the learner has thought through the solution for the problem. The *learner* should plan the procedure for every job he undertakes in the shop. He should read the drawing or design, or make the drawing if none is available, make his own bill of materials, and determine the costs. He should list the major steps of construction in their proper sequence, and the needed tools. The plan of procedure should be written on note paper or on a special card, which the instructor should check carefully to see that the learner has planned a logical procedure, and that he has set up what seems to be an adequate solution for

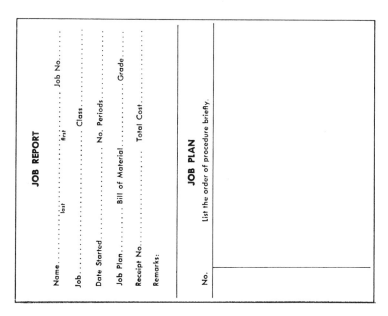

Fig. 19. *A job report card (original size 6 by 10 in.).*

his problem. The written plan of procedure is the control by means of which the teacher determines how well the learner has thought through the job from beginning to end. Such planning is not easy for it involves reasoning of a high type. It is what anyone who does creative work must do before starting a new project. The lawyer, doctor, engineer, architect, teacher, orator, musician, artist, anyone doing creative work, must plan carefully in advance if his proposed effort is to meet with success. Pencil and paper may not always be necessary for planning all activities outside of school, but planning itself is necessary. In teaching it is necessary to have a device that will provide a means of checking on the learner's problem-solving efforts—therefore a written form is used.

The form shown in Figure 19, either printed or mimeographed, is used extensively. It is easily filed or recorded. The place for the material bill may be arranged so that it can be torn off and filed separately for material accounting. The remainder of the card can be left with the learner for reference on the job.

Consider the making of a plan of procedure for constructing a one-quart dipper of sheet metal. The learner should make the plan of procedure and have it approved before he starts work. The order of doing the work may be written in terms of work patterns. It is not necessary to list the exact operations. The learner has not assimilated them in that way. Several operations may combine in the learner's thinking. A series of statements that indicate a sequence in his thinking is satisfactory. Some teachers recommend that the learner check against the list of units for the course. This seems unwise since he should be held to account for his learning to date. There are many factors that should be taken into account in making the dipper. He must determine whether he should fold the seam before he forms to shape or afterward. He must decide whether he will form the shape or solder the seam before he puts the wire in the top or turns the burr for the bottom. The determination of answers to these questions involves a background of experiences from which the learner must draw. It is evident that it will be necessary for the teacher at times to assist the student by calling attention to certain facts or conditions that may have been overlooked and to assist in relating ideas and experiences in order to secure a satisfactory plan.

Start Early

Training in making the plan of procedure should start with the beginning projects. During these lessons the teacher should give special attention to planning, so that the learner can learn to plan while he learns the operations. The planning may be simple at first; experience has shown that it can begin as early in the laboratory as in other subjects.

The learner should be taught early that planning is an ability which is highly essential for success in the laboratory and in the world outside of school. He should learn also that he will be held to account for everything he has been taught, and that he will be expected to draw from his accumulated learning for each project he undertakes. The extent and thoroughness of accumulated experience and intelligence will determine the speed and accuracy of planning. Planning will improve with each succeeding project, and with progress in the subject there will be some very valuable behavior changes.

Planning does not take the place of instruction on operations and information topics, but it does create a state of readiness for needed instruction. The form of instruction may be oral, written, or through visual aids. The greater the variety of stimuli available for teaching a lesson, the greater are the possibilities of coping with individual differences in learning.

Summary

Success in the world is closely associated with ability to do purposeful and effective thinking, to solve problems peculiar to a given activity. School instruction, therefore, should include problem-solving experiences in all offerings. Teachers in various technical areas share this responsibility.

Mathematics sets the pattern for the approach to problem-solving in most areas of human effort. Fundamental elements in mathematics, combined in patterns brought about by purposeful thinking, solve problems. Fundamental elements in technical work must also be combined into patterns in order to do creative work. These elements are quite constant, but the problems are variable and will continue to change. Machines may expedite the work, but the principle of problem-solving remains.

The making of a plan of procedure is the place for emphasis in problem-solving in shop teaching. Operations, for safety reasons, should be taught by the instructor. Trial and error in teaching most operations is not problem-solving, it is a dangerous procedure.

Training in making plans of procedure should start with the beginning projects. The teacher should teach how to plan, just as he teaches other important lessons. Planning creates a readiness for instruction on new lessons.

ASSIGNMENTS AND DISCUSSION TOPICS

1. What areas in education should include problem-solving experiences in the offerings?
2. Distinguish *what to think* from *how to think*.
3. What is the pattern of action in all problem-solving?
4. Compare problems in mathematics with problems in the technical laboratory.
5. When should instruction start in planning procedures?
6. Should new operations be learned by discovery so purposeful thinking can be developed?
7. What should be included in the plan of procedure?

FOR FURTHER READING

Anderson, H. H., ed., *Creativity and Its Cultivation* (New York: Harper and Brothers, 1959), Chap. 11 by E. R. Hilgard.

Baysinger, G. B., and Silvius, G. H., *The Student Planning Book* (Princeton, N. J.: D. Van Nostrand Co., 1960).

Dyal, J. A., *Readings in Educational Psychology* (New York: McGraw-Hill Book Co., 1962), Chap. 8.

Ferns, G. W., and Anderson, A. D., "Problem Solving and Designing," *School Shop*, Vol. 19, No. 9, May, 1960, pp. 12–13, 42.

Fryklund, Verne, C., "The Ongoing Objective," *Industrial Arts and Vocational Education*, May, 1955, pp. 147–149.

——— "Incidence of Problem Solving in Shop Teaching," *Education*, Vol. 55, No. 8, April, 1935, pp. 464–467.

Kendler, H. H., *Basic Psychology* (New York: Appleton-Century-Crofts, 1963), Chap. 11.

Miller, Rex, and Smalley, Lee H., *Selected Readings in Industrial Arts* (Bloomington, Ill.: McKnight and McKnight Publishing Co., 1963).

Parnes, S. J., and Harding, H. F., *A Source Book for Creative Thinking* (New York: Charles Scribner's Sons, 1962).

Selvidge, R. W., and Fryklund, V. C., *Principles of Trade and Industrial Teaching* (Peoria: C. A. Bennett Co., 1946), Chap. 16.

Silvius, H. G., and Bohn, R. C., *Organizing Course Materials* (Bloomington, Ill.: 1961), Chap. 6.

Stephens, J. M., *Educational Psychology* (New York: Henry Holt and Co., 1959), Chaps. 9, 10.

Williams, W. A., *Accident Safety Manual for Shop Teachers* (Chicago: American Technical Society, 1963).

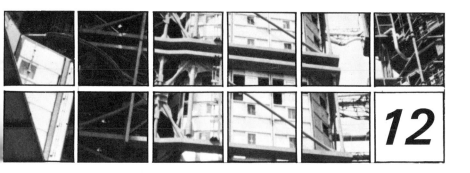

Written Instructions

The instruction sheet is mentioned so frequently in connection with the study of the analysis technique that it hardly seems appropriate to write *finis* to a book on analysis without discussing it. Therefore, in order that the student of analysis may conclude his study of this book with some measure of understanding of the relation of the instruction sheet to analysis, this chapter is presented. The person who has contributed most to the development of the instruction sheet is Selvidge.[1]

It is not necessary for all learning to be acquired through lectures and demonstrations in school. Much is to be learned outside of school through the printed page. Guided study by means of well-written instruction sheets creates readiness for, and establishes authenticity of, instruction to be gained through the printed page. Successful use of well-written instruction sheets and technical books brings improvement in reading habits and is therefore

1. R. W. Selvidge, *Individual Instruction Sheets* (Peoria: Manual Arts Press, 1926).

to be encouraged. For those who wish to keep abreast of technological changes and to advance in their work, education must continue after formal schooling is over; and it is through study of technical literature that technicians can improve their status.

Analysis Is Necessary

It should seem now to the reader that occupational analysis is one of the most useful of curriculum instruments in technical education. One should study analysis before attempting to write instruction sheets or technical books. One would then learn that in every activity complicated enough to require instruction there are elements of manipulative or informational nature, or both. Identification of these elements, as has been learned in this book, is necessary because they form the basis for lessons. Whether a lesson is manipulative or informational, it must be taught by some means. In a given teaching situation there may be a demonstration, a drawing or diagram, a reading assignment in a book, or an instruction sheet, a visual aid, and so on, but whatever the instructional device, analysis is necessary to identify the elements to be taught. The materials obtained through analysis, therefore, form the outlines for writing instruction sheets, books, and preparing visual aids. A well-written set of instruction sheets compose a good technical book. Several good books now available were originally written as instruction sheets.

A Valuable Teaching Aid

The instruction sheet is a teaching device the writing and use of which has come to be an inviting problem to students, teachers, supervisors, and administrators of technical teaching. There are difficulties in writing and in using good instruction sheets, and yet their value is generally recognized.

The problems arising with instruction-sheet writing and their use seem of more concern to technical teachers than do many other instructional problems. Much hope is held out for their usefulness, and consequently there is much interest. The interest is growing despite the problems that seem to arise. Generally, well-written sheets accompanied by good judgment in using them are valuable in all classes and schools.

The Writing Difficulty

One of the major causes of difficulty relating to instruction sheets is in the writing, and poorly written sheets are of little use. The technical teacher often lacks ability to write because, like most people, he dislikes writing, and writing instruction sheets requires training, experience, and perseverance. Most persons who have the urgent desire and stick-to-it-iveness can learn to write, but it is not an overnight achievement.

An understanding of composition is essential. The person who wants to learn to write instruction sheets should review the more common principles of good writing. Instruction-sheet writing provides practical application for the seemingly abstract principles of composition and grammar.

The instruction sheet must have in it good sentence structure and accurate word usage so that it will be understood and will command respect from those who use it. The learner must pass to the laboratory from academic classes where good books are used and where attention is given to English usage. Poorly written sheets, besides being difficult to understand, also engender disrespect for the technical offerings. If the content of technical subjects is as poorly conceived and taught as it is often represented in some written instruction sheets, there certainly can be little to say for the quality of such instruction. Teaching without instruction sheets can be less harmful than teaching with poorly written sheets. The inadequacies of oral expression seem to fade, but the errors and inaccuracies of written expression remain in their original form. Instruction can be provided on how to do technical writing, and intensive effort must be put into it by both the teacher and the student of writing. Just as there are classes in methods of teaching, analysis, course development, and so on, there also are classes for those who desire to learn to do technical writing.

Use of Written Instructions

A good measure of common sense is necessary in using instruction sheets even when they are well written. Applying common sense can be thought of as applying good psychology. A sheet should not be passed out to a learner for the first time without supervision of its use. This would be about as successful with most learners as giving a demonstration by calling a group together without general readiness or attention before proceeding. Just as there is a correct technique in writing instruction sheets, so is there a correct technique in using them.

It is difficult to find a more interesting and useful device than the demonstration for presenting the instruction covering an operation. The demonstration has long been used in teaching, but it has not been successful by itself in coping with individual differences in learning. Since learners vary greatly in achievement, there comes a time when good books, instruction sheets or visual aids must be relied upon for complete success. The demonstration becomes less effective with large groups as the class continues to its advanced stages of achievement. If a class is large and if individuals must have instruction separately, and if achievement is at many stages, then the well-written instruction sheet is useful. It is not a perfect device, but there is much in its favor.

Most learners dislike obtaining technical information from the printed page, especially if someone is ready to provide the desired information orally. Advancement in technical work outside of school is largely based on ability to gather information readily from the printed page. We can do much, therefore, in training young people for future advancement, by making use of printed instructional materials. This statement does not assume, however, that we should be lavish in our production of written materials. Instruction sheets should be prepared when needed, but they must be very well written if they are to be helpful.

A good procedure to follow in the use of instruction sheets, assuming, of course, that they really contain the needed instructions, is to begin using them the first meeting of the class. If the demonstration of an operation is under consideration, and an operation sheet is available, let one learner read the sheet, step by step, while another learner, or the teacher, goes through the steps that are explained. This will show the class that the instruction sheet really contains the desired directions. It also proves to what extent the sheet is thoroughly prepared. The average learner doubts the helpfulness of most written instructions before using them, and actual use before a group proves their worth. It is a good plan to continue the guided group use of the sheets for several lessons in order to establish them. This would apply to use of a technical book also.

When a learner obviously has not read the sheet, and yet asks the instructor for some desired information, he should be directed to the sheet. If necessary, the instructor or another learner should read the sheet to him to show that the needed information is there. Too much readiness on the part of the teacher to give orally what is available in printed form lessens the learner's chance to develop in the use of the printed instructions.

A Supplementary Teaching Device

There are many variables in the make-up of individuals which contribute to individual differences. Of most concern to teachers are the differences in student rates of learning. In technical classes, learning is individual and the rate of progress is not the same in any two individuals. Good psychology points to the use of a variety of instructional devices, and demands readiness on the part of the teacher to match each situation at hand. Intelligence, previous experience, and a practical understanding of human nature all suggest the need of using the immediately appropriate devices in expediting instruction.

The instruction sheet should be thought of as one of the many devices, rather than just one, which supplements the personal instruction of the teacher. It is a supplementary device. At no time, even in its early use, was it thought of as taking the place of the teacher.

Simplicity Is Important

It has been mentioned that in analysis, as in teaching, simplicity is necessary. In the writing of instruction sheets, simple directness is exceedingly important. A learner is confronted with many complex situations that tend to confuse and retard his efforts, and the emphasis should be on the side of simplifying rather than complicating the learning situation. Any instruction, whether oral or written, should be simple in form. Certainly the demonstration must be simply presented, and inasmuch as the instruction sheet is intended to supplement the demonstration, it too must be simple. A common cause of failure and discouragement in the use of instruction sheets is their complexity. Frequently this happens because the untrained writer attempts to make the sheets formal and profound. Not only should the written instructions be simple in language, they must also be simple in organization.

Who Should Write Instruction Sheets

The teaching of technical subjects could be advanced if considerable study were given by those responsible to the problem of writing better instruction sheets. Written instruction sheets are needed, but in view of the difficulties that frequently accompany attempts at writing them, with or without training, there probably should be a limitation of their production. Group efforts should be encouraged, however, because pooled judgments and criticisms are helpful, and because writing instruction sheets is difficult for one person. It is good experience for a teacher to write instruction sheets under guidance and criticism. Such writing makes him take stock of his knowledge of and ability to perform a given operation.

Committee work is desirable. However, the membership of committees should include those who are actively interested and who will give time to study the literature dealing with written instructions. It is wise to select only those who are willing to rewrite and re-create their materials until these can be understood by the students who are supposed to learn from them. Membership in writing committees should also include those who not only will give constructive criticism, but who will also take it without feeling that personal faultfinding is involved. The professional attitude should prevail.

When good sheets have been produced and tried, they should be made available for general use in a school system. Instruction covering the essential elements should be made available in every possible form. Teachers want such materials. Most teachers do not have a great deal of time to write, and therefore they welcome group efforts in the production and distribution of good sheets. Of course, good books are most economical and best in the long run.

Official recognition of the value of committee work should not result in the exclusion of individual efforts. Naturally, individual effort is desirable, and should be encouraged, but pooled efforts increase the speed of production of teaching materials. Moreover, successful individual effort makes successful group effort. Frequently, specialized abilities appear in a group. One person may be competent in sketching, another in writing, another in analyzing, and so on. By distributing efforts in this way, in terms of specialized abilities, the writer has had much satisfaction in producing written instructions following the initial classwork covering the principles of writing them.

Kinds of Instruction Sheets

There are many kinds of written instruction sheets. Some represent careful planning and study of the problem; others represent little planning and little study. The most widely known and accepted classification of written instructions came from Selvidge.[2] The term *instruction sheet* is properly applied to all forms of written instructions. One form should not be assumed as representative of all others, nor should all forms of sheets take the name of one of the special types. For example, it is not unusual to hear the term "job sheet" mentioned in reference to any form of instruction sheet. A *job sheet* is one of the special forms of instruction sheets. Selvidge classified instruction sheets as follows.[3]

1. OPERATION SHEET. This sheet gives definite step-by-step instructions for performing an operation. If one were to provide a complete set of operation sheets for teaching an industrial occupation, there would be an operation sheet covering every operation. A sheet is not written for use in the production of any particular job, but rather for use on any job that requires the particular operation. It has flexible application. The listing of the operating steps obtained in the analysis of the activity is the first step in making an operation sheet.

The title of the operation sheet is the name of the operation, and it comes from the analysis. A typical title taken from the machine shop is "To Knurl." This title constitutes the objective of the lesson. The purpose of the sheet is as specific as is indicated by the title. This one is assumed to provide instruction on how to knurl on any job that requires knurling.

2. *Ibid.*
3. *Ibid.*, Chap. I.

2. *INFORMATION SHEET.* This sheet covers the instruction involved in an information topic. The three kinds of information topics can be presented conveniently by means of information sheets. Simple statements that include necessary facts without unnecessary discussion form the content.

The title for an information sheet is taken from the list of information topics in the analysis of the occupation. That is, the name of an information topic is the title of the information sheet. The content is simply presented, and questions are provided to facilitate study and class discussion. References are given so that further study can be made of the topic.

3. *ASSIGNMENT SHEET.* This is one of the most useful of instruction sheets. It is used, as the name suggests, to direct study and investigation. It is particularly helpful in teaching mathematics, science, and drafting. Instruction in all shop activities can be facilitated with this sheet.

An assignment sheet usually includes a statement and explanation of the principle to be taught with examples of its application. Assignments of problems are offered for application of the principle under instruction; or in another form, depending on what is to be taught, a list of questions covering a topic for investigation is presented. Directions are given telling how to find the answers.

4. *JOB SHEET.* This term is often mistakenly used in referring to any kind of instruction sheet. A job sheet is intended to cover instruction for a particular job. Inasmuch as many operations are likely to be included in a given job, complete instructions would be more economically handled by means of operation sheets.

A job sheet includes a statement of the job to be done, a job specification, a list of tools and materials, questions, references, and a series of directions for doing the job. The latter usually consist of general directions to do each step without telling precisely how to do them. Job sheets are most helpful on job assignments that involve very little specific instruction on skills and when production is more important than learning.

Experienced teachers believe that the job sheet might better be a plan of procedure made by the learner before attacking a new job. This provides excellent opportunity for building proper attitudes of attack on new problems. After all, the learner should be taught to read drawings, make bills of materials, determine the tools needed for a given job, and the procedure he proposes to follow in construction. It would seem that that is what he should be trained to do in learning his occupation. The job sheet does this for him, and thus deprives him of an important learning opportunity. The job sheet has valuable uses, but giving instructions on performance of skills and planning procedures is not among them.

Writing Helps

The following information is presented for those who need at least a small measure of first aid in writing instruction sheets.

1. Plan the instruction sheet carefully before you start to write This is important. It will save considerable rewriting and time.

In planning, first outline each successive instructional unit. If the unit is an operation, list the steps in the exact sequence of their performance by listing words or phrases that could be used as a checklist while writing. It will be necessary for you to visualize the procedure, or to work in your shop, when making the operation analysis. This preliminary checklist is exceedingly important. While making the preliminary checklist, make note of steps that will need sketches or pictures for clarification. If you have already made an analysis according to the plan recommended in this book, you will have the necessary outlines for writing instruction sheets, for preparing visual aids, or writing a technical book.

2. In writing, make direct statements as though you were telling someone or giving an order "to do something." The directions should be definite and brief without sacrificing good sentence structure. The word sequence should follow the movement in performance. The step, or part of a step, which you wish emphasized or carried out first in performance should be placed first. Articles of speech, such as "a" and "the," *should not be omitted*. Good sentence structure is as necessary in technical literature as elsewhere. This was not important in the listing of operating steps in the analysis in Chapter 8, but it is now.

3. Do not mix major points of theory and performance. Merely tell how to do each step in the operation, but do not discuss each step.

4. Unnecessary statements should be avoided. Illustration: "*Now having filled the pen*, draw vertical lines." The words in italics are not necessary to direct the learner to "draw vertical lines." "Now" suggests that in a previous step you told how to fill the pen.

5. Use the dictionary. Correct word selection is essential to writing instruction sheets. Check the spelling carefully. Remember that written instructional materials should be carefully prepared. They are a long time in print and cannot readily be remade.

6. Do not be satisfied with the first attempt at writing an instruction sheet. This holds true of all writing. The best writers do not use the first draft. They write and rewrite and allow intervals of time between attempts. Mistakes are more easily discovered when the composition is examined after the writer has been away from the task a day or two.

7. Instruction sheets may be written by the teacher who uses them, but he should be sure that the methods described follow standard practice. His students may go out in competition with others, and peculiar methods may be a hindrance to their progress. When in doubt, check your procedures with various books and with competent persons. The safest and the most economical way of utilizing time and materials should be the criteria for determining the validity of a method of performing an operation.

8. It is not necessary to write a specification for an operation sheet. Specifications belong with jobs and job sheets. Furthermore, it is not necessary to write the reasons for teaching an operation. The learner usually knows the reason which underlies the necessity for learning the operation.

9. Be careful of copyright infringements. A few words together, a picture, or an altered picture taken from any book or magazine article is evidence to show that there is infringement of copyright. Use your own composition of words and your own pictures. It is the safe way and the professional way.

10. Use sketches and illustrations to clarify written descriptions, but do not depend upon sketches alone without accompanying written descriptive material. Identify the sketches by marking them with the word "Figure" and a number. Place a descriptive

legend below each sketch to help the learner see the connection right away. This legend should consist of words taken from the accompanying instruction sheet.

11. Do not describe a "second method" of performing an operation. If there is a second method, it should be good enough to form the basis for another sheet.

12. Write "CAUTION" in capital letters at the point where there is likely to be danger or breakage. The word *caution* is a warning of danger; in print it is the equivalent of a red flag. Do not give it a number. It is part of the step in which the danger lies. Use "Note" if you wish to emphasize or call attention to a point in performance. Use notes sparingly and they will serve their purpose well. All statements should be important enough, however, not to require emphasis under "Note." Do not use "Caution" for "Note."

13. Place the sketches on the left side of the paper, keeping them as close to the descriptive material as you can. A good sketch placed close to the words describing it makes the sheet more easily understood, and therefore more usable and interesting.

14. Ask someone to read your sheet after you have made every effort to perfect it. Be ready to take suggestions for improvement. Even expert writers do this. On the other hand, when you help someone, be professional in your suggestions. Do not feel that you must find something wrong. Commendation and criticism belong together in preparation of instruction sheets, or any technical writing.

15. More than one sheet may be used in writing one unit. Number all sheets so that you can always tell whether a page is missing. If there are three pages, let page one be "1 of 3," page two "2 of 3," and so on.

16. Management problems are greatly reduced if you bind or clip together all sheets to be used in a particular class.

Summary

A well-written instruction sheet is one of the most useful of supplementary teaching aids. Considerable attention should be given to the proper use of instruction sheets, especially when instruction with them is first attempted. Merely handing a sheet to a learner with a request to use it does not assure readiness on the part of the learner to use it. There must be supervision of the initial attempts. A good way to begin the use of instruction sheets is to have one learner read the directions to another who follows them in performing the operation. This shows that the sheet really contains the instruction it is supposed to contain.

Instruction sheets are difficult to write. Unless one is trained to write, or is willing to be trained and will persevere, it is desirable to leave the writing to others. Committee or group preparation is suggested.

Instruction sheets must be simple in organization and simply presented. Complex arrangement and wordy presentation should be avoided. There are four major types of instruction sheets according to Selvidge. They are (1) operation sheets, (2) information sheets, (3) assignment sheets, and (4) job sheets. A few directions of a first-aid, practical nature for writing are presented.

ASSIGNMENTS AND DISCUSSION TOPICS

1. Give illustrations of need for instructional devices other than the group demonstration.
2. Name helpful devices other than instruction sheets and discuss their values.
3. List and discuss advantages and disadvantages of instruction sheets. Present them at the blackboard and encourage discussion on the points enumerated.
4. Consider the causes of individual differences and their implication for teachers of vocational subjects.
5. Consider your own field of work and the various things you could do to cope with individual differences in learning and acquiring skill.
6. Discuss difficulties and hindrances attending production of written instructions, individual or group.

FOR FURTHER READING

Carlsen, R. M., "Individual Instruction Sheets," *Industrial Arts and Vocational Education*, Vol. 23, No. 9, September, 1934, pp. 269–272.
Copyright Law of the U.S.A., 1960 (Washington, D. C.: Superintendent of Documents).

Editorial: "Ethics of Shop-Made Instruction Sheets," *Industrial Education*, Vol. 33. No. 4, October, 1930, pp. 105–108.

Giachino, J. W., and Gallington, R. O., *Course Construction in Industrial Arts and Vocational Education* (Chicago: American Technical Society, 1961), Chap. 17.

Glidden, H. H., *Reports, Technical Writing, and Specifications* (New York: McGraw-Hill Book Co., 1964).

Henig, M. S., "Individualizing the Instruction," *Industrial Arts and Vocational Education*, Vol. 24, No. 11, November, 1935, pp. 325–326.

Hicks, T. G., *Successful Technical Writing* (New York: McGraw-Hill Book Co., 1959).

Levine, I. H., "Solving Reading Problems in Vocational Subjects," *High Points*, April, 1960, pp. 10–17.

Metz, J. J., ed., "Instruction Sheet and Textbook," *Industrial Arts and Vocational Education*, Vol. 20, No. 5, May, 1931, pp. 178–179.

Selvidge, R. W., *Individual Instruction Sheets* (Peoria: C. A. Bennett Co., 1926).

Selvidge, R. W., and Fryklund, V. C., *Principles of Trade and Industrial Teaching* (Peoria: C. A. Bennett Co., 1946), Chaps. 6, 7, 13, 18.

Silvius, G. H., and Bohn, R. C., *Organizing Course Materials* (Bloomington, Ill.: McKnight and McKnight Publishing Co., 1961), Chap. 10.

Struck, F. T., *Creative Teaching* (New York: John Wiley and Sons, 1938), Chaps. 2, 3, 14.

Van Westrienen, H. J., "Handling Large Classes," *Industrial Arts and Vocational Education*, Vol. 22, No. 8, August, 1933, pp. 245–249; Vol. 22, No. 9, September, 1938, pp. 282–284.

Appendix

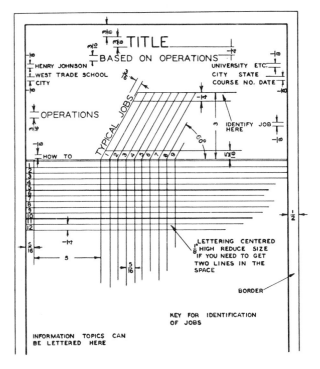

The form above offers a handy arrangement for listing typical jobs and indicating an analysis of the operations to be performed. The chart may be made any size by extending the number of "job" columns to the right and adding to the number of "operations" lines at the bottom. After the chart has been checked, it may be copied on tracing cloth and blueprinted.

209

Index

Education, and industry, 17f
Employment, changes in, 23

Flow charts, 39, 40; in systems analysis, 45

Habits, and learning, 160; and occupational expert, 2; of work, 169f
Herbartian steps, 166f

Inductive teaching, 187
Industrial workers, modern, 5, 17
Industry, and education, 17; education for, 3
Information, kinds of, 70ff; card, 143f; outline, 132ff; related, 67ff
Information sheet, 202; teaching aids, 196
Instructional order, arranging, 98ff
Instructional steps, listing, 117ff
Instructions; kinds of, 201; who should write, 200; written, 164, 195ff
Instruction, units of, 153

Job, classification, 42; definition, 49ff; descriptions, 34ff; operations, 63; payroll, 53, 62; report, 189; sheets, 202; specifications, 37

Learning and teaching, 7, 157ff
Lecture, 167
Lesson, teaching, 165
Levels of attainment, 103

Management, class, 169
Materials, and operating steps, 122f
Mathematics, 8, 186; sets pattern, 186f

Mechanics, and operatives, 21ff; training of, 28
Methods, and course development, 175
Motion and time study, 39

Observations, 165
Occupational elements, constancy of, 60; identifying, 49
Occupations, blocking, 90ff; custom, 87ff; service, 180ff
Operations, auxiliary, 58; cumulative nature of, 59ff; definition of, 53ff; expressing an, 56f; identifying, 61f; job, 63; payroll jobs, 62; and processes, 62; and skills, 61; teaching criteria, 120
Operation sheet, 201f
Operatives, in industry, 24; abilities of, 27; training of, 28
Organization charts, 39; in systems analysis, 45
Orientation, and course development, 177
Outline, information, 132f
Outlook, technical occupations, 19f

Plan of procedure, 188
Preparation, 166
Presentation, 167
Problem-solving, 8; 185ff; not inductive teaching, 187f
Procedure, plan of, 188f
Processes, and operations, 62f
Professional preparation, 46
Progress, recording of, 105ff
Progression factors, 102f
Psychology, elementary, 157ff

Questions, asking, 168f

Recitation, 165